CHEM 341L

Organic Chem I Lab

University of North Dakota

Author: Michael W. Rapp

CENGAGE
Learning·

Australia • Brazil • Japan • Korea • Mexico • Singapore • Spain • United Kingdom • United States

CHEM 341L: Organic Chem I Lab, University of North Dakota

Signature Labs
Michael W. Rapp

For product information and technology assistance, contact us at
Cengage Learning Customer & Sales Support, 1-800-354-9706

For permission to use material from this text or product,
submit all requests online at **cengage.com/permissions**
Further permissions questions can be emailed to
permissionrequest@cengage.com

This book contains select works from existing Cengage Learning resources and was produced by Cengage Learning Custom Solutions for collegiate use. As such, those adopting and/or contributing to this work are responsible for editorial content accuracy, continuity and completeness.

Compilation © 2017 Cengage Learning

ISBN: 978-1-337-44923-6

Cengage Learning
20 Channel Center Street
Boston, MA 02210
USA

Cengage Learning is a leading provider of customized learning solutions with office locations around the globe, including Singapore, the United Kingdom, Australia, Mexico, Brazil, and Japan. Locate your local office at:
www.international.cengage.com/region.

Cengage Learning products are represented in Canada by Nelson Education, Ltd.

For your lifelong learning solutions, visit **www.cengage.com/custom.**

Visit our corporate website at **www.cengage.com.**

Printed in the United States of America
9 10 11 12 13   27 26 25 24 23

Brief Contents

Practicing Safety in the Organic Chemistry Laboratory

Prepared by Michael W. Rapp, University of Central Arkansas

PURPOSE

Review the basic rules of laboratory safety. Recognize the common hazards in an organic chemistry laboratory. Learn the proper responses to incidents that may occur in the laboratory.

SAFETY RULES FOR THE ORGANIC CHEMISTRY LABORATORY

Follow all rules. A Safety Contract is included within this module. You must hand in a completed contract to indicate your willingness to follow the standard rules of laboratory safety before you will be allowed to work in the laboratory.

1. *Wear safety goggles while in the chemistry laboratory.* Use splash-proof goggles rated as ANSI Z87.1. Goggles are to be worn over prescription glasses. Supply your own goggles because sharing goggles can lead to eye infection from another wearer. Use of contact lenses under the goggles is discouraged because contact lenses may increase the damage done if an irritant gets in your eye. If you must wear contact lenses under your goggles to avoid unreasonably limited vision, indicate that need on your Safety Contract.

2. *Wear proper clothing to provide protection from reagent spills.* Long pants are required and long-sleeved shirts are preferred. A laboratory coat that extends below the knee is recommended. Shoes must be closed-toe and made of nonporous material. Do not wear loose-fitting clothing because it may catch on objects and cause spills. Avoid loosely woven or fuzzy fabrics because they increase the chances of fire hazard to the wearer. Tie back hair that is longer than shoulder length.

3. *Use good housekeeping practices to ensure a safe workplace.* Call to the attention of the laboratory instructor any conditions that seem unsafe. Avoid cluttering the work area, especially the work areas shared by

many students. Place personal items, such as coats and backpacks, in separate storage areas rather than in the laboratory work space. Return items promptly to their proper locations. Disassemble and clean glassware directly after use because residues in glassware may become resistant to cleaning if not washed promptly. Allow hot glassware to cool to room temperature before washing.

4. ***Do only authorized experiments, and work only when the laboratory instructor or another qualified person is present.*** Do not enter the laboratory until the laboratory instructor is present. Unauthorized experimenting will waste time and may expose you and others to unreasonable risk. Authorized experimental procedures take into account the special hazards of the materials used. Do not treat laboratory reagents and equipment as playthings. Do not remove any reagents from the laboratory. Injuries from laboratory incidents most often occur from violations of the precautions given in this paragraph.

5. ***Treat all laboratory reagents as if they are poisonous and corrosive, unless told otherwise.*** *Immediately wash spills off your skin* with plenty of water. Then notify your laboratory instructor. This response is especially important for many organic compounds because their fat solubility enhances their ease of absorption through the skin. Wash your hands thoroughly with soap or detergent before leaving the laboratory. Special hazards of laboratory reagents will be indicated by appropriate labels on the reagent bottles.

   Containers from chemical supply companies may use the National Fire Protection Association's diamond or some similar indicator of potential hazard, as shown in Figure 1. A number from 0 (low) to 4 (high) in each category indicates the degree of hazard.

6. ***Dispense reagents carefully and dispose of laboratory reagents as directed.*** Do not use reagents from unidentified containers. Double check each label before dispensing a reagent. To prevent contamination, do not return any reagent to its original container. Place any excess reagent in the recovery container provided by your laboratory instructor. Dispose of reagents as directed by the laboratory instructor and the written procedure. Promptly notify the laboratory instructor of any spill. Clean up a spill *only if directed* to do so by your laboratory instructor. Spills should be cleaned up immediately to prevent contact of the chemicals with persons who are not aware of the spill. When

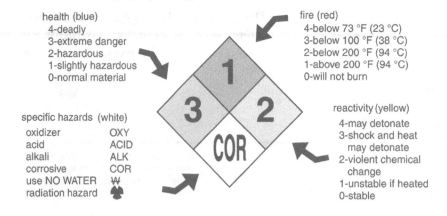

Figure 1
National fire protection association label

health (blue)
4-deadly
3-extreme danger
2-hazardous
1-slightly hazardous
0-normal material

fire (red)
4-below 73 °F (23 °C)
3-below 100 °F (38 °C)
2-below 200 °F (94 °C)
1-above 200 °F (94 °C)
0-will not burn

specific hazards (white)
oxidizer   OXY
acid   ACID
alkali   ALK
corrosive   COR
use NO WATER   W
radiation hazard

reactivity (yellow)
4-may detonate
3-shock and heat
  may detonate
2-violent chemical
  change
1-unstable if heated
0-stable

weighing reagents, dispense them into containers so that reagents do not spill onto the balance.

7. *Do not eat, drink, use tobacco, or apply cosmetics in the laboratory.* Violation of this rule can introduce poisons into your system. Especially avoid any contamination to your mouth or eyes. Never bring food or drinks into the laboratory.

8. *Immediately report all incidents to the laboratory instructor.* An **incident** is any situation in the laboratory that might endanger those persons present. Your laboratory instructor must give prompt attention when injuries occur. Even minor incidents may require attention. The laboratory instructor may also be able to use the information you provide to help other students avoid a similar difficulty.

9. *Be familiar with the location and use of all safety equipment in the laboratory.* All laboratories should have an eyewash station, a safety shower, a fume hood, and more than one fire extinguisher. Anticipate the steps to be taken in the event of an incident. Prompt response to an incident can make the difference between a minor event and permanent injury. The laboratory instructor may direct you to assist in responding. However, do not place yourself or others at risk in order to respond to an incident in the laboratory. A subsequent section describes proper responses to incidents in the laboratory.

10. *Become familiar with each laboratory assignment before coming to the laboratory.* Pay particular attention to cautions given in the procedure and by the laboratory instructor. Use of some equipment presents special hazards. For example, vacuum operations include the possibility of implosions, and ultraviolet light is damaging to the eyes if viewed directly. Each laboratory experiment will give special cautions for any hazardous reagents used in that experiment. Your laboratory instructor will provide other information and reminders as needed.

By law, chemical supply companies must provide a **Material Safety Data Sheet (MSDS)** with each reagent they sell. The MSDS is a technical bulletin that gives detailed information on the properties of a laboratory reagent. Some information from an MSDS for 1-propanol is shown in Figure 2 on the next page. Your laboratory instructor may have you consult the reagent MSDS as part of your laboratory work.

COMMON HAZARDS IN THE ORGANIC CHEMISTRY LABORATORY

Anticipate common hazards encountered in the laboratory. Experience has shown that ignoring the following *common concerns* will lead to mishaps.

1. Never pipet by mouth. Many organic chemicals are toxic.

2. Do not use chipped or cracked glassware, which may cause cuts or may crack and spill its contents unexpectedly.

3. Obtain approval from your laboratory instructor before starting a distillation. Make certain the apparatus has an opening. Do not heat a closed apparatus because abrupt release of the increased pressure may propel reagents or pieces of glass at persons nearby. Use a fresh boiling

MATERIAL SAFETY DATA SHEET

ANY SCIENTIFIC COMPANY   EMERGENCY #: (800)-555-XXXX
YOURTOWN, USA

Section 1 (Identity): 1-PROPANOL (and synonyms given) Mol. Formula C_3H_8O Mol. Wt. 60.1
   CAS # 71-23-8   NFPA Ratings (scale 0–4): Health = 1, Fire = 3, Reactivity = 0

Section 2 (Hazardous Ingredients): 1-PROPANOL (100%)
      Exposure Limits: 200 ppm (492 mg/m^3) OSHA TWA
                250 ppm (614 mg/m^3) OSHA STEL

Section 3 (Physical & Chemical Characteristics): Description: Colorless liquid with mild alcohol odor
   Boiling Point: 207 F (97 C)   Melting Point –195 F (–125 C)   Vapor Pressure (20 C): 15 mm Hg
   Odor Threshold: 30 ppm

Section 4 (Physical Hazards): Dangerous fire hazard when exposed to heat or flame. Vapors are heavier
   than air and may travel a considerable distance to a source of ignition. Flash Point: 74 F (23 C) (CC)
   Upper Explosive Limit 13.7%   Fire Fighting Media: Dry chemical, carbon dioxide, water spray, or alcohol-
   resistant foam.   Transportation Data: US DOT Hazard Class 3 — flammable liq.

Section 5 (Reactivity): Stable under normal temperatures and pressures. Incompatibles: alkali & alkaline
   earth metals. Attacks coatings, plastics, and rubber.

Section 6 (Health Hazards — Inhalation, Skin Contact, Eye Contact, and Ingestion):
   INHALATION: Irritant/Narcotic. 4000 ppm is immediately dangerous to life or health.
   Acute Exposure: Inhalation of vapors may cause moderate irritation of the upper respiratory tract with
      coughing and shortness of breath. High concentrations may cause CNS depression, with dizziness,
      headache, and vomiting.
   Chronic Exposure: Reproductive effects have been reported.
   First Aid: Remove from exposure area. Perform artificial respiration if necessary. Get medical attention immed.

Section 7 (Precautions for Safe Handling and Use — Storage, Disposal, Spill & Leak Procedures):
   May be ignited by electrostatic sparks, so should be stored in grounded container, as specified in NFPA
   77-1983. Disposal must be in accordance with 40 CFR 262 (EPA Hazardous Waste Number D001). For small
   spills, take up with sand or other noncombustible absorbent and place into containers for later disposal.

Section 8 (Control Measures — Ventilation, Firefighting, Clothing, Gloves, Eye Protection): Wear
   appropriate protective clothing and equipment to prevent prolonged skin contact.

Figure 2
Selected information from MSDS for 1-propanol

chip each time a liquid is boiled to avoid **bumping**, the sudden eruptive release of vapor. Such a release can burn persons nearby. Do not heat any distillation pot to dryness because the residue that remains may be heat sensitive, and overheating could cause it to detonate. Also, glassware that is superheated could crack. Before heating a flask, clamp the neck of the flask to support it in an elevated position to allow withdrawal of the heat source and rapid cooling, if needed.

4. Lubricate and clamp ground glass joints so they will not freeze or spring open in use. Use lubricant sparingly.

5. Do not point the open end of a container at anyone. Abrupt formation of bubbles, such as from boiling, could propel the contents into a person's face.

6. Place heated glass and other hot objects on an appropriate surface, such as a wire gauze or ceramic pad, until they have cooled. Hot glass

or metal may look like cool glass or metal, so cautiously touch objects that have been heated before handling them. Place a note nearby any hot objects remaining at the end of a laboratory period, so students in a subsequent laboratory period will not be endangered.

7. Use a fume hood when working with reagents whose vapors are harmful. Except for small quantities heated by steam or a hot-water bath, heating of highly flammable organic substances in open containers must be done in a hood. In using a fume hood, position any apparatus well within the hood space, keeping your head outside the hood. The flow of air through the hood must be adequate and unobstructed. The hood sash should be lowered, except when making manipulations within the hood. Place within the hood only those items necessary for the operation being performed. Keep the exhaust fan on as long as any reagents remain within the hood.

8. When testing odors of reagents, gently waft vapors from the container toward your nose. Do not directly sniff the contents of a container.

9. Do not use open flames (Bunsen burners) in the presence of flammable materials, especially organic solvents such as acetone, diethyl ether, or petroleum ether. Use of a flameless heat source diminishes the danger of a fire, but such heat sources remain hot for quite some time after they are turned off. Overheated sand baths, hot plates, or heating wells can ignite fumes from volatile organic solvents.

10. Wear gloves when dispensing irritating reagents. This precaution is especially important for organic reagents, which can penetrate the skin readily. Your laboratory instructor will designate gloves that are appropriate for the reagents to be used. Latex surgical gloves are not appropriate because they allow passage of many organic reagents. Gloves should be inflated to check for breaks by whipping them through the air. Do not check gloves by inflating them by mouth.

11. Take special care when working with strong acids or strong bases. Contact with these materials can cause severe chemical burns. Prepare dilute acids by slowly adding the concentrated acid to a larger volume of water, with stirring. The water dissipates the evolved heat and prevents localized boiling that could spew the contents from the container.

12. If you must insert glass tubing into stoppers, follow the directions given by your laboratory instructor.

RESPONSES TO INCIDENTS IN THE ORGANIC CHEMISTRY LABORATORY

Become familiar with actions to be taken in the event of incidents in the laboratory. Provide appropriate assistance to others in emergencies. The items that follow describe the actions that should be taken in certain situations.

1. Report all incidents to the laboratory instructor, who is responsible for actions to be taken in response to incidents and for reports to be made to other authorities. As defined in Safety Rule 8, an incident is any

© 1997 Cengage Learning

situation in the laboratory that might endanger those persons present. An improper response may change a trivial difficulty into a much more hazardous situation. Sometimes an irritation or personal injury is not manifested immediately. A student who experiences an irritation later in the day, and who has a reasonable suspicion that contact with laboratory reagents could have caused the problem, should contact the laboratory instructor or a health care professional for advice.

The safety of persons in the laboratory has absolute priority over all other considerations. While you will not have the responsibility for directing others in the laboratory, you should be aware that the typical sequence of actions to take in the event of an incident in the laboratory is *ALERT, CONFINE,* and *EVACUATE.* If you are the first to notice a hazard in the laboratory, you should *alert* your laboratory instructor and others nearby. After you and others are clear of danger, your laboratory instructor will *confine* the hazard. If the hazard persists, the laboratory instructor may give instructions to *evacuate* the area.

Severe injuries may result from unreasonable responses to unexpected situations. For example, a person who spills a corrosive reagent on himself or herself might hope no one else notices, waiting until leaving the laboratory to wash off the spill. In the meantime, the burn from the reagent may have progressed from a superficial irritation to one that requires medical attention. Or a person who has lifted a test tube at the time the contents ignite might throw the tube through the air onto another person, catching that person's clothes on fire. Consider the consequences of your actions.

2. Dispose of broken glass as directed by the laboratory instructor. Use a hand brush and dust pan to collect the pieces. Do not attempt to gather sharp glass by hand. Place broken glass in specially designated receptacles in order to avoid placing other persons at risk. Place very small, sharp objects—for example, syringe needles and pieces of capillary tube—in specially designated receptacles.

   If a mercury thermometer is broken, step back from the work area and notify the laboratory instructor, who will use special techniques to collect the spilled mercury. The special hazard with mercury is not from contact with the skin, but from prolonged exposure to the vapor. A cut by a broken thermometer should get the same attention as other cuts.

3. For either minor cuts or burns, wash the affected area using soap or detergent. Tissue damage from a superficial burn will be minimal if the affected area is cooled quickly, so you should flush the affected area with cold water. Then notify the laboratory instructor. When work is resumed, protect any break in the skin by wearing a glove, in order to prevent introduction of laboratory reagents.

4. In the event of a reagent spill, notify the laboratory instructor. Appropriate steps to be taken in response to a reagent spill will vary, depending on the amount and identity of the reagent. Concerns for hazards other than the reagent itself, such as danger of shorting electrical equipment, may even take precedence. Spills of organic solvents may be a fire hazard. In such an event, remove all ignition sources, including any equipment that could produce a spark—for example, switches being turned on and off. Hot plates and sand baths at a high

temperature do not cool rapidly on turning off, so move these heat sources away from the spill. If a spill creates a large amount of fumes, evacuate the laboratory. Stop any experiments, if doing so doesn't place anyone at risk.

Deal promptly with reagent spills on a person. Wash the affected area with large volumes of water. Rapid response is necessary because many organic solvents are fat soluble and can be absorbed through the skin. Use the sink or safety shower as needed, depending on the size of the spill. Remove clothing and wash skin with soap or detergent to complete the removal of the reagent. Do not remove goggles before washing any reagent spill from the face, to lessen the likelihood of getting the reagent in the eyes.

A person whose eyes have had reagents splashed into them requires assistance from others. A person's automatic response to an irritation to the eyes is closing of the lids and rubbing, actions that will only increase the irritation. Other persons should assist the person to the eyewash fountain and operate the water flow, while the person holds open his/her eyelids. The flow of water must get to the entire eye surface, continuing for twenty minutes. Cold water may be intolerable for such an uninterrupted period, so periodic washing may have to be done. Irrigation of the eye will not be adequate if contact lenses that are present are not removed. Further treatment of irritation to the eye from a reagent spill must be done only by a health care professional.

5. Many common solvents used in the organic chemistry laboratory are highly flammable, and a small fire may occur in the laboratory. Do not react without thinking. The immediate response to a fire in the laboratory is to take those actions that remove individuals from the hazard. For example, stepping back from a small fire and cautioning neighbors of the hazard would be a reasonable response. Move flammable materials away, and turn equipment off or remove equipment from the vicinity of the fire. Shut off the gas spigot or heating element. Place a watch glass or beaker over a small container to smother the burning material. Some *small* fires, such as alcohol fires, may be allowed to burn out.

If a fire spreads to a larger area of the bench, the laboratory instructor or other authorized persons should operate the fire extinguisher. Should a fire reach a stage where it cannot be easily controlled, the laboratory instructor will direct you to evacuate the laboratory and the building.

The most distressing incidents in laboratories are those where an individual is on fire. Using small quantities of flammable substances and following safe practices in the laboratory ensure that such an event is unlikely to happen. Proper response can make the difference between loss of some clothing or, in the extreme case, loss of life. If a person's lungs are seared from inhaling flames, there will be little chance of recovery.

The safety shower or water from the sink may be sufficient to extinguish a fire on a person. In a severe situation, the proper response to fire on an individual's clothing is to *STOP, DROP, and ROLL.* That is, if you have fire on your body, *stop* where you are, *drop* to the floor, and *roll* to smother the flames. Staying upright will allow the flames to rise to the face. Nearby persons can use a laboratory coat to beat out the flames. When the flames are extinguished, remove any smoldering fabric. If the person has been burned, place the person under the safety shower. Other persons nearby can assist as needed, such as extinguishing fire on the bench, shutting off equipment, and cleaning up. Most other persons in the laboratory should simply move away.

6. Ingestion or inhalation of a reagent will likely require the assistance of a health care professional. In such an event, immediately notify the laboratory instructor, who will gather the information needed to report the incident to the poison control center. Space is provided at the end of this module for you to record the phone number of the poison control center in your area.

    Avoid the inhalation of unsafe levels of irritating or toxic vapors by following the directions for using laboratory reagents and by using the reagents in a fume hood. While you must not depend upon your senses to alert you to inadvisable conditions, notify your laboratory instructor promptly if your eyes begin to sting or if you develop a headache that may be caused by fumes in the laboratory. Especially avoid breathing the vapors from chlorinated solvents and aromatic compounds.

7. Immediately notify the laboratory instructor if you or a neighbor feels faint. A person who has become unconscious from inhalation of fumes must be removed from the source of the fumes. Other than checking the person's airway and treatment for shock (elevating limbs, keeping warm), further treatment should only be made by a health care professional.

This module is to serve only as a starting point for good safety practices and does not purport to specify minimum legal standards or to attest to the accuracy or sufficiency of the information contained herein, and the publisher assumes no responsibility in connection therewith.

Safety Information

Complete this form and keep it for possible use.

1. Emergency health providers (telephone numbers to call)
Campus Health Services:

on campus _____   off campus _____

Emergency Medical Assistance:

on campus _____   off campus _____

State Poison Control Center: _____
Campus Police:

on campus _____   off campus _____

City Police or Fire Department:

on campus _____   off campus _____

2. Contacting the laboratory instructor

Name: _____   Office: _____

Office phone: on campus _____   off campus _____

Home phone: _____   E-mail address: _____

3. Reporting incidents (for reference)

The following information will be needed when communicating with health professionals and/or recording incidents.

Nature of the incident (description – including fire, substances involved, number of individuals involved and their physical conditions):

Individuals involved (identification – name, gender, age):

Location of the incident, including who will meet any emergency vehicle, and where:

Person reporting the incident (name, phone number being used to report the incident. *Note*: Do not allow this phone to be tied up for calls unrelated to control of the incident.):

Safety Contract

Complete this form and give to your laboratory instructor.

I have carefully read the organic chemical laboratory safety module. I have given my answers to the accompanying safety quiz and given that completed quiz to the laboratory instructor as an indication of my familiarity with the module. Whenever I am in an area where laboratory reagents are being used, I agree to abide by the following rules:

1. Wear safety goggles.
2. Wear proper clothing.
3. Use good housekeeping practices.
4. Do only authorized experiments, and work only when the laboratory instructor or another qualified person is present.
5. Treat laboratory reagents as if they are poisonous and corrosive.
6. Dispense reagents carefully. Dispose of laboratory reagents as directed.
7. Do not eat, drink, use tobacco, or apply cosmetics in the laboratory.
8. Report all incidents to the laboratory instructor.
9. Be familiar with the location and use of all safety equipment.
10. Become familiar with each laboratory assignment before coming to the laboratory.
11. Anticipate the common hazards that may be encountered in laboratory.
12. Become familiar with actions to be taken in the event of incidents in the laboratory.

_____   _____
student signature   date

_____   _____
laboratory instructor   date

In the space below, give any health information, such as pregnancy or other circumstance, that might help the laboratory instructor provide a safer environment for you, or that could aid the laboratory instructor in responding to an incident involving you in the laboratory.

1. I do/do not (circle one) expect to wear contact lenses during laboratory work. [*Note*: Goggles must still be worn when contact lenses are worn.]

2. List any known allergies to medication or other chemicals.

name   section   date

Safety Quiz

1. On a separate sheet of paper, sketch the layout of the laboratory. (a) Note the location of each important safety feature (fire extinguisher, fume hood, eye wash, safety shower, and exits). (b) Draw a line from your work location, showing the path you would take to evacuate the laboratory. (c) Indicate the nearest location where you can activate the fire alarm.

2. Describe the steps to be taken in the event 10 mL of ethanol in a 50-mL beaker ignites in the laboratory.

3. Identify two important reasons for notifying the laboratory instructor of any incidents that occur in laboratory.

4. Why is unauthorized experimenting by a student in the laboratory not allowed?

5. Describe the steps to be taken in the laboratory if a large bottle of acetone (noncorrosive, nontoxic, highly volatile, water-soluble, flammable solvent) is broken and spilled.

6. According to the information in the MSDS (Figure 2), which hazardous category (health, fire, or reactivity) is of greatest concern for 1-propanol?

7. What is the first action to be taken in the event a person spills some reagent on himself or herself? What is the second action to be taken?

8. Identify three precautions to be taken before beginning the distillation of an organic liquid.

Measuring the Melting Points of Compounds and Mixtures

Prepared by Joseph W. LeFevre, SUNY Oswego

PURPOSE OF THE EXPERIMENT

Measure the melting points of pure benzoic acid and pure mandelic acid. Determine the eutectic composition and the eutectic temperature of benzoic acid–mandelic acid mixtures. Identify an unknown compound using mixture melting points.

BACKGROUND REQUIRED

None

BACKGROUND INFORMATION

The **melting point** of a compound is the temperature at which the solid is in equilibrium with its liquid. A solid compound changes to a liquid when the molecules acquire enough energy to overcome the forces holding them together in an orderly crystalline lattice. For most organic compounds, these intermolecular forces are relatively weak.

The **melting point range** is defined as the span of temperature from the point at which the crystals first begin to liquefy to the point at which the entire sample is liquid. Most pure organic compounds melt over a narrow temperature range of 1–2 °C.

The presence of a soluble impurity almost always causes a decrease in the melting point expected for the pure compound and a broadening of the melting point range. In order to understand the effects of impurities on melting point behavior, consider the melting point–mass percent composition diagram for two different fictitious organic compounds, X and Y, shown in Figure 1. The vertical axis represents temperature and the horizontal axis represents varying mass percent compositions of X and Y.

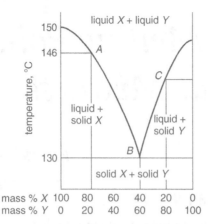

Figure 1

Melting point–mass percent composition diagram for a two-component mixture

Both compounds have sharp melting points. Compound X melts at 150 °C, as shown on the left vertical axis, and Y melts at 148 °C, as shown on the right vertical axis. As compound X is added to pure Y, the melting point of the mixture decreases along curve CB until a minimum temperature of 130 °C is reached. Point B corresponds to 40 mass percent X and 60 mass percent Y and is called the **eutectic composition** for compounds X and Y. Here, both solid X and solid Y are in equilibrium with the liquid. The **eutectic temperature** of 130 °C is the lowest possible melting point for a mixture of X and Y. At temperatures below 130 °C, mixtures of X and Y exist together only in solid form.

Consider a 100-microgram (µg) mixture composed of 20 µg of X and 80 µg of Y. In this mixture, X acts as an impurity in Y. As the mixture is heated, the temperature rises to the eutectic temperature of 130 °C. At this temperature, X and Y begin to melt together at point B, the eutectic composition of 40 mass percent X and 60 mass percent Y. The temperature remains constant at 130 °C until all 20 µg of X melts. At the eutectic temperature, X and Y will melt in the ratio of 40 parts X to 60 parts Y. If 20 µg of X melts, then 30 µg of Y (20 µg X × 60/40 ratio = 30 µg Y) also melts. At this point, the remaining 50 µg of solid Y (80 µg – 30 µg = 50 µg) is in equilibrium with a molten mixture of the eutectic composition.

As more heat is applied to the mixture, the temperature begins to rise, and the remaining Y begins to melt. Y continues to melt as the temperature increases, shown by curve BC.

Finally, at 142 °C, point C, where the liquid composition is 20 mass percent X and 80 mass percent Y, all of Y is melted. At temperatures higher than 142 °C, liquid X and liquid Y exist together with a composition of 20 mass percent X and 80 mass percent Y. Thus, the melting point at which the entire mixture liquefies is 142 °C, six degrees lower than the melting point of pure Y. Also, the melting point range 130–142 °C is quite broad.

In the previous example, X acts as an impurity in Y. Compound Y can also act as an impurity in X, as indicated in Figure 1 earlier in this experiment. For example, in a mixture composed of 80 µg of X and 20 µg of Y, the mixture begins to melt at the eutectic temperature of 130 °C. As before, at this temperature, the eutectic composition is 40 mass percent X and 60 mass percent Y. The temperature remains at 130 °C until all 20 µg of Y melts. At the eutectic temperature, X and Y will melt in the ratio of 40 parts X to 60 parts Y. Thus, if 20 μg of Y melts, 13 μg of X (20 μg $Y \times 40/60$ ratio = 13 μg X) also melts.

The remaining 67 μg of X (80 μg – 13 μg = 67 μg) melts over the range of 130 –146 °C, shown by curve BA. At 146 °C, the last traces of X melt. This melting range is larger than the range over which 20 mass percent X and 80 mass percent Y melts.

If a mixture has exactly the eutectic composition of 40 mass percent X and 60 mass percent Y, the mixture shows a sharp melting point at 130 °C. Observing this melting point could lead to the false conclusion that the mixture is a pure compound. Addition of either pure X or pure Y to the mixture causes an increase in the melting point, as indicated by curve BA or BC, respectively. Observing this melting point increase indicates that the original sample is not pure.

The initial melting that occurs at the eutectic temperature is sometimes very difficult to observe. This difficulty is especially true if only a small amount of an impurity is present, because the quantity of liquid produced at the eutectic temperature is very small. However, the temperature at which the last trace of solid melts can be accurately measured. Hence, a sample with a small amount of impurity will have an observed melting point much higher than the eutectic temperature, but lower than that of the pure compound.

Because the melting point of a compound is a physical constant, the melting point can be helpful in determining the identity of an unknown compound. A good correlation between the experimentally measured melting point of an unknown compound and the accepted melting point of a known compound suggests that the compounds may be the same. However, many different compounds have the same melting point.

A **mixture melting point** is useful in confirming the identity of an unknown compound. A small portion of a known compound, whose melting point is known from the chemical literature, is mixed with the unknown compound. If the melting point of the mixture is the same as that of the known compound, then the known and the unknown compounds are most likely identical. A decrease in the melting point of the mixture and a broadening of the melting point range indicates that the compounds are different. A flowchart for using a mixture melting point to identify an unknown compound is shown in Figure 2.

Melting points can also be used to assess compound purity. A melting point range of 5 °C or more indicates that a compound is impure. Purification of the compound causes the melting point range to narrow and the melting point to increase. Repeated purification may be necessary before the melting point range narrows to 1–2 °C and reaches its maximum value, indicating that the compound is pure.

Measuring Melting Points

In practice, measuring the melting point of a crystalline compound involves several steps. First, a finely powdered compound is packed into a melting point capillary tube to a depth of 1–2 mm. Then the capillary tube containing the sample compound is inserted into one of several devices used to measure melting points.

Figure 3(a) shows the Thiele tube apparatus, filled to the base of the neck with silicone oil or mineral oil. The capillary tube is attached to a thermometer so that the sample is located next to the middle of the

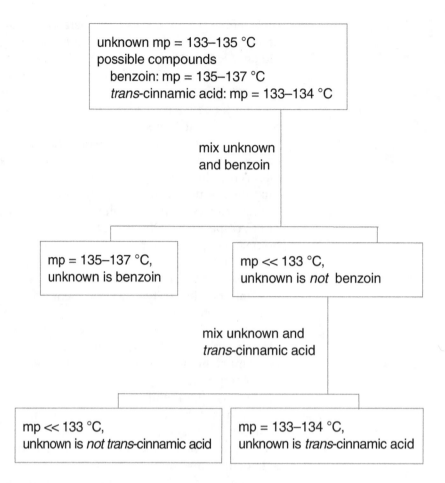

Figure 2

Flowchart for mixture melting point determination of an unknown

thermometer bulb. The thermometer is inserted into the oil and then the side arm of the Thiele tube is heated with a Bunsen burner flame.

The Thomas–Hoover Uni-Melt device, shown in Figure 3(b), contains silicone oil that is stirred and heated electrically. Silicone oil can be heated to temperatures up to 250 °C. With this device, up to seven samples can be analyzed at one time.

The Mel-Temp apparatus, shown in Figure 3(c) consists of an aluminum block that is heated electrically. The aluminum block can be heated easily to temperatures up to 400 °C, and can tolerate temperatures up to 500 °C for brief time periods. A thermometer and up to three samples can be inserted into the block at one time. A light and magnifier permit easy viewing of the sample(s).

If the melting point of the compound is unknown, it is convenient to first measure the approximate melting point of the compound, called the **orientation melting point.** The sample is heated at a rate of 10–15 °C per minute until it melts. Then the melting point apparatus is cooled to approximately 15 °C below the orientation melting point. A new sample is heated, increasing the temperature at a much slower rate of 1–2 °C per minute, to accurately measure the melting point. A slow heating rate is necessary because heating a sample too rapidly may cause the thermometer reading to differ from the actual temperature of the heat source. The

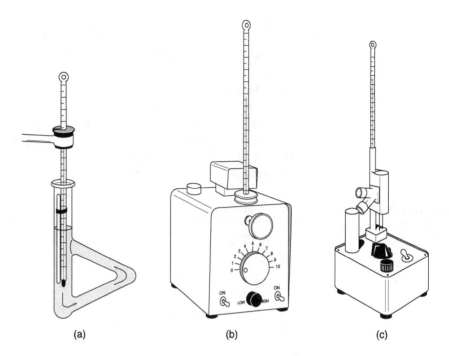

Figure 3
Different types of melting point apparatus: (a) Thiele tube; (b) Thomas–Hoover; (c) Mel-Temp

(a)   (b)   (c)

result would be an observed temperature reading that differs from the actual melting point temperature.

If the melting point of the sample is known, the sample can be quickly heated to within 10–15 °C of its melting point. Then the heating rate can be slowed to increase 1–2 °C per minute until the sample melts.

Errors in observed melting points often occur due to a poor heat transfer rate from the heat source to the compound. One cause of a poor heat transfer rate is the placement of too much sample into the capillary tube. Finely ground particles of the compound are also necessary for good heat transfer. If the particles are too coarse, they do not pack well, causing air pockets that slow heat transfer.

Sometimes slight changes, such as shrinking and sagging, occur in the crystalline structure of the sample before melting occurs. Also, traces of solvent may be present due to insufficient drying and may appear as droplets on the outside surface of the sample. This phenomenon is called **sweating** and should not be mistaken for melting. The initial melting point temperature always corresponds to the first appearance of liquid within the bulk of the sample itself.

Some compounds decompose at or near their melting points. This decomposition is usually characterized by a darkening in the color of the compound as it melts. If the decomposition and melting occur over a narrow temperature range of 1–2 °C, the melting point is used for identification and as an indication of sample purity. The melting point of such a compound is listed in the literature accompanied by *d* or *decomp*. If the sample melts over a large temperature range with decomposition, the data cannot be used for identification purposes.

Some compounds pass directly from solid to vapor without going through the liquid phase, a behavior called **sublimation.** When sublimation occurs, the sample at the bottom of the capillary tube vaporizes and recrystallizes higher up in the capillary tube. A sealed capillary tube is used to take the melting point of a compound that sublimes at or below its melting point. The literature reports the melting point for these compounds accompanied by *s*, *sub*, or *subl*.

In this experiment you will measure the melting points of benzoic acid, mandelic acid, and mixtures of these two compounds. Both compounds melt near 122 °C. You will use these data to construct a melting point–mass percent composition diagram. From this diagram, you will estimate the eutectic temperature and eutectic composition for benzoic acid and mandelic acid. Finally, using the mixture melting point method, you will identify an unknown compound.

Measuring the Melting Points of Compounds and Mixtures

Equipment

graph paper	metric ruler (mm)
marking pen	microspatula
melting point capillary tubes	2 watch glasses

Reagents and Properties

Substance	Quantity	Molar mass (g/mol)	mp (°C)	bp(°C)
benzoic acid	10 mg	122.12	122–123	249
mandelic acid	10 mg	152.15	120–122	

Preview

- Measure the melting point of benzoic acid
- Measure the melting point of mandelic acid
- Measure the melting point range of four mixtures containing various amounts of benzoic acid and mandelic acid
- Obtain a sample of an unknown compound
- Measure an orientation melting point and an accurate melting point of your unknown compound
- Obtain a sample of each of two substances appearing in Table 1 that have melting points similar to your unknown
- Prepare a mixture of your unknown compound and each of your selected compounds
- Measure the melting point of each mixture
- Identify your unknown compound

PROCEDURE

CAUTION

Wear departmentally approved safety goggles at all times while in the chemistry laboratory.

Always use caution in the laboratory. Many chemicals are potentially harmful. Prevent contact with your eyes, skin, and clothing. Avoid ingesting any of the reagents.

1. Measuring Melting Points of Benzoic Acid and Mandelic Acid

CAUTION

Benzoic acid is an irritant.

Place 2–3 mg of benzoic acid on a clean, dry watch glass. If the compound is not a fine powder, pulverize it using a microspatula.

CAUTION

Capillary tubes are fragile and easily broken.

Load a melting point capillary tube by pressing the open end of the tube into the powder. Pack the powder into the closed end of the tube by tapping the closed end against the bench top. Repeat the cycle of loading and packing until you can see 1–2 mm of benzoic acid through the tube.

NOTE: Make certain that no more than 1–2 mm of compound is placed in the capillary tube. A larger amount will give a melting point range that is too large.

To ensure good packing, drop the capillary tube with the open end up through a 1-m-long piece of glass tubing onto the bench top. Repeat several times. Place the capillary tube in the melting point apparatus provided by your laboratory instructor.

Because pure benzoic acid melts at 122–123 °C, heat the capillary tube rapidly to 110 °C. Then slow the heating rate to 1–2 °C per min. Record the temperature at which liquid first appears in the bulk of the sample and the temperature at which the entire sample becomes liquid.

NOTE: Heating the capillary tube too quickly near the melting point will result in an inaccurate melting point measurement.

CAUTION

The capillary tubes are hot. Allow them to cool enough to avoid burning your fingers.

When finished, remove the capillary tube. Place all used capillary tubes in the container labeled "Discarded Capillary Tubes", provided by your laboratory instructor.

Obtain 2–3 mg of mandelic acid and measure the melting point following the procedure described for benzoic acid. Pure mandelic acid melts at 120–122 °C.

2. Determining the Eutectic Temperature and Composition of a Benzoic Acid–Mandelic Acid Mixture

From your laboratory instructor, obtain four benzoic acid–mandelic acid mixtures of the following compositions:

	Percent benzoic acid	Percent mandelic acid
mixture 1	80	20
mixture 2	60	40
mixture 3	40	60
mixture 4	20	80

Using a marking pen, carefully label a capillary tube for each mixture. For example, near the top of the tube, mark the tube that will contain mixture 1 with one horizontal line. Similarly, mark the tubes for mixtures 2–4 with two, three, and four lines, respectively. Load each mixture into its capillary tube as previously described.

Place the capillaries containing mixtures 1 and 2 into the melting point apparatus. Heat the samples rapidly to 80 °C. Then slow the rate of increase to 1–2 °C per min. *Carefully* observe and record the temperature at which the crystals first begin to melt and the temperature at which the last trace of crystals melts.

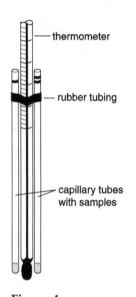

Figure 4
Attachment of two capillary tubes to a thermometer

(thermometer, rubber tubing, capillary tubes with samples)

NOTE: If you are using a Thiele tube, place the samples to the left and right of the thermometer bulb. Secure them in place with a small ring of rubber tubing, as shown in Figure 4. Make certain the bottom of the capillary tube is positioned vertically near the midpoint of the thermometer bulb. Also, be certain the rubber tubing and pen marks are 2–3 cm above the oil surface because the oil expands when heated.

NOTE: If you are using a Mel-Temp apparatus, you will need to lift the samples a few millimeters above the base and slowly rotate the samples to see the last trace of crystals melt. Be careful not to break the capillary tubes.

Allow the apparatus to cool to 80 °C and repeat the melting point measurements, using the capillaries containing mixtures 3 and 4.

3. Identifying an Unknown Compound by Mixture Melting Point

CAUTION

Unknowns may be flammable, toxic, and irritating.

Obtain 10 mg of an unknown compound from your laboratory instructor and record its identification code. Pulverize the sample, label and load a capillary tube, and take an orientation melting point. Cool the apparatus to 15 °C below its orientation melting point. Prepare a new sample, and accurately measure the melting point.

From Table 1 (on the next page), identify the two compounds that have melting points closest to the melting point of your unknown compound. Obtain a few milligrams of each of these compounds. Place one known compound on a clean, dry, labeled watch glass. Add an approximately equal amount of your unknown compound.

Table 1 *Melting points of compounds used as unknowns*

Compound	mp (°C)	Compound	mp(°C)
benzhydrol	65–67	*trans*-cinnamic acid	133–134
biphenyl	69–72	benzoin	135–137
phenanthrene	99–101	benzilic acid	150–153
o-toluic acid	103–105	adipic acid	152–154
acetanilide	113–115	benzanilide	164–166
fluorene	114–116	4-bromoacetanilide	167–169
(*R,S*)-mandelic acid	120–122	4-hydroxybenzoic acid	215–217
benzoic acid	122–123	anthracene	216–218

Similarly, place the other known compound on a second watch glass and add an approximately equal amount of your unknown. Pulverize and mix each sample thoroughly, using a clean microspatula each time. Load the samples into separate, labeled capillary tubes. Also, load two capillary tubes with pure unknown.

Take the melting point of one of the mixtures and the pure unknown *simultaneously*. Quickly heat the samples to within 30 °C of the pure compound's melting point. Then slow the heating rate increase to 1–2 °C per min.

Repeat the procedure using the other mixture. Compare your data and identify your unknown.

4. Cleaning Up

Use the labeled collection containers provided by your laboratory instructor. Wash your glassware with soap or detergent.

CAUTION

Wash your hands thoroughly with soap or detergent before leaving the laboratory.

---

name   section   date

Post-Laboratory Questions

1. Using the data from Parts 1 and 2 of the Procedure, plot on graph paper the *upper temperatures* of the melting point ranges for benzoic acid and mandelic acid on the left and right vertical axes, respectively, as was done in Figure 1 for compounds *X* and *Y*. Plot the *upper temperatures* of the melting point ranges of the four mixtures on the same graph, using the proper mass percent of each compound on the horizontal axis. Use a temperature range of 80–130 °C on the vertical axis. From the graph, determine the approximate eutectic temperature and eutectic composition of a benzoic acid–mandelic acid mixture.

NOTE: Draw straight lines through the points, one straight line through the points for benzoic acid, mixture 1, and mixture 2; another straight line through the points for mandelic acid, mixture 3, and mixture 4. Do not attempt to curve lines as shown in Figure 1.

---

2. Using the melting point–mass percent composition diagram you drew for Question 1, identify the approximate melting point ranges for benzoic acid–mandelic acid mixtures of the following compositions.

   (a) 90:10

   (b) 70:30

   (c) 30:70

   (d) 10:90

3. Describe in detail the melting point behavior of the 80:20 benzoic acid–mandelic acid mixture.

4. Devise a flowchart similar to the one in Figure 2 to show how you identified your unknown.

5. Using your textbook or another appropriate resource, find the structural formula for your unknown. Make a drawing of the formula.

6. Briefly explain why you were told to simultaneously measure the melting points of the mixtures and of the pure unknown in Part 3 of the Procedure.

_____   _____   _____

Pre-Laboratory Assignment

1. Briefly identify or explain

(a) two useful functions served by knowing the melting point of an organic compound.

(b) why a finely powdered sample should be used in a melting point measurement.

(c) why it is important to heat a sample slowly to obtain an accurate melting point.

(d) two reasons why it is sometimes difficult to measure the temperature at which the crystals first begin to liquefy.

(e) what two effects a soluble impurity usually has on the melting point of a compound.

(f) what occurred when crystals began to disappear from the bottom of the capillary tube rather than turning to a liquid.

2. A sample has an experimental melting point of 100–101 °C. Can you conclude that the sample is pure? Briefly explain your reasoning.

3. Using Figure 1, explain in detail the melting point behavior of a mixture composed of 60 mass percent X and 40 mass percent Y.

4. An unknown compound melted at 131–133 °C. It is thought to be one of the following compounds (mp, °C): *trans*-cinnamic acid (133–134); benzamide (128–130); DL-malic acid (131–133); or benzoin (135–137). The mixture melting points of the unknown compound with each of the test compounds are listed below. What is the unknown compound? Briefly explain your reasoning.

Unknown plus	mp range (°C)
trans-cinnamic acid	110–120
benzamide	130–132
DL-malic acid	114–124
benzoin	108–116

5. Using your textbook or another appropriate resource, find the structural formula for benzoic acid and mandelic acid. Draw the structural formulas of these compounds.

Purifying Acetanilide by Recrystallization

Prepared by Carl Wigal, Lebanon Valley College

PURPOSE OF THE EXPERIMENT

Select an appropriate recrystallizing solvent. Separate and purify acetanilide from a mixture by recrystallization. Compare the melting points of impure and recrystallized acetanilide.

BACKGROUND REQUIRED

You should know how to measure mass, in milligrams, and volume, in milliliters. You should know how to measure melting points.

BACKGROUND INFORMATION

Impurities often contaminate organic compounds that have been synthesized in the laboratory or isolated from natural sources. **Recrystallization** is a purification process used to remove impurities from organic compounds that are solid at room temperature. This process is based on the premise that the solubility of a compound in a solvent increases with temperature. Conversely, the solubility of the compound decreases as the solution cools, and crystals form.

Very pure compounds can be produced by recrystallization. As a heated solution of the desired compound cools, a small, pure seed crystal of the compound forms in the solution. Layer by layer, additional molecules attach to this crystal, forming a growing crystal lattice, as shown in Figure 1. The molecules in the crystal have a greater affinity for other molecules of the same kind than they do for any impurities present in the solution. In effect, the process of crystal formation removes one kind of molecule from the solution.

Choosing a Recrystallizing Solvent

Selecting an appropriate recrystallizing solvent to use is probably the most difficult step of recrystallization. The primary consideration when choosing a recrystallizing solvent is the extent to which the compound and impurities

Figure 1

(a) Identical molecules attach to one another, forming a crystal lattice; (b) impurities have different shapes or sizes and do not layer

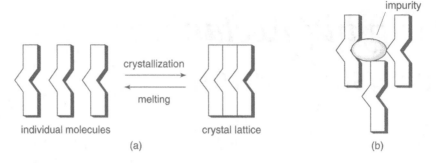

Figure 2

Ideal solubility patterns of a compound, line A, and accompanying impurities, lines B and C, at varying temperatures

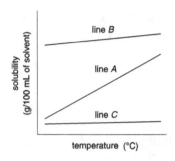

are soluble in the solvent at high and low temperatures. The graph in Figure 2 shows three possible scenarios for how the solubilities of the compound and the impurities depend on temperature.

Ideally, the compound to be recrystallized should be very soluble in the chosen solvent at elevated temperatures, but almost insoluble in the cold solvent, as shown by line *A*. Impurities should be soluble in the chosen solvent at all temperatures so that impurities stay in solution, as shown by line *B*. Alternatively, impurities should be insoluble at all temperatures so they can be filtered from the hot solution, as shown by line *C*.

Experimentation is needed to select an appropriate recrystallizing solvent. Typically, several solvents are used to test the extent of solubility of the compound. A small amount of the compound is mixed with a few milliliters of each solvent. The compound's solubility is observed at room temperature and near the solvent's boiling point. If the compound is soluble in a solvent at room temperature, the solvent is not suitable. If the compound is insoluble at room temperature and soluble near the solvent's boiling point, the solvent is a suitable candidate.

"Insoluble" is a relative term. All compounds are soluble to some extent in every solvent. For example, benzoic acid in water has a solubility of 6.80 grams per 100 milliliters at 100 °C. However, benzoic acid has a solubility of only 0.34 gram per 100 milliliters in water at 25 °C. Benzoic acid is typically listed as insoluble in 25 °C water.

When considering the solubility of an organic compound, a general rule is *like dissolves like*. Polar organic molecules contain functional groups that can hydrogen bond, such as $-OH$, $-NH_2$, and $-CO_2H$. Polar molecules are generally most soluble in polar solvents. Many organic molecules are nonpolar. Nonpolar molecules are most soluble in nonpolar solvents. A list of commonly used recrystallization solvents is shown in Table 1.

The boiling point of the recrystallization solvent should be lower than the melting point of the compound to be recrystallized. If the solvent's boiling point is higher than the compound's melting point, the compound will oil out. **Oiling out** occurs when a compound is insoluble in a solution at a temperature above the compound's melting point. As a result, the compound is deposited as an oil, and not as crystals.

Another important criterion for selecting a recrystallizing solvent relates to recovery of the compound. An abundant quantity of crystals must be produced as the solution cools to room temperature or below.

The four major criteria for selecting a recrystallizing solvent are summarized in Table 2.

Table 1 *Commonly used recrystallization solvents, in order of decreasing polarity*

Solvent	bp(°C)	Solvent	bp(°C)
Water	100	Ethyl ether	35
Methanol	65	Dichloromethane	40
Ethanol (95%)	78	Toluene	111
Acetone	56	Petroleum ether	35–60
Ethyl acetate	77		

Table 2 *Criteria for selecting a recrystallizing solvent*

(1) Compound being purified must be insoluble in solvent at room temperature

(2) Compound must be soluble in boiling solvent

(3) Solvent's boiling point must be lower than the compound's melting point

(4) An abundant quantity of crystals must be recoverable from the cool solvent

Often, the requirements necessary for successful recrystallization are not met by a single solvent. In these cases, a mixture of two solvents, called a **solvent pair,** is used. Two solvents are selected that are miscible with each other, but have opposite abilities to dissolve the compound. The compound to be recrystallized should be soluble in one solvent (*A*) of the pair and should be relatively insoluble in the second solvent (*B*).

To determine the proper combinations of the two solvents, the compound is dissolved in a minimum volume of solvent *A* near the boiling temperature of this solvent. Next, solvent *B* is added to the boiling mixture until the mixture becomes cloudy, indicating that the compound is precipitating from solution. A few drops of solvent *A* are added to redissolve the precipitate, producing a clear solution. Then the solvent pair is treated just like a single recrystallization solvent. Common solvent pairs are ethanol and water, acetone and ether, and acetic acid and water.

Dissolving the Compound

Once a suitable solvent is found, the recrystallization process is continued by dissolving the compound in a minimum volume of boiling solvent. Then a five percent excess of the solvent is added to the saturated solution to prevent premature crystallization. For example, if 10 mL of a boiling solvent is required to *just* dissolve a compound, five percent of 10 mL or 0.5 mL would be added to bring the total volume to 10.5 mL.

Decolorizing the Solution

Occasionally, a sample may contain a soluble impurity that produces a colored solution, and that solution colors crystals that would otherwise be colorless. In that case, activated carbon, or decolorizing carbon, is used to remove these colored impurities from solution. Activated carbon has a

Figure 3
A gravity filtration apparatus used to filter undissolved impurities

surface area that adsorbs dissolved organic substances. Adding an excess of carbon must be avoided, because carbon can also adsorb the compound that is being recrystallized, reducing the percent recovery.

The hot solution is filtered by gravity filtration through a funnel containing a fluted filter paper to remove any insoluble compound, including the carbon. If no undissolved impurities are present, or if carbon has not been added, the filtration step is omitted. A typical gravity filtration apparatus is shown in Figure 3. The funnel, filter paper, and collection flask are heated with boiling solvent prior to filtering the solution to prevent premature crystal formation.

Using a *fluted* filter paper increases surface area inside the funnel and speeds the filtering process. Figure 4 on the next page shows how to produce a fluted filter paper.

Recrystallizing Pure Compound

After the compound is dissolved in a minimal amount of boiling solvent and the solution is filtered, as necessary, the solution is allowed to slowly cool to room temperature. If crystal formation occurs too rapidly, impurities may become trapped in the crystals. Then the filtered solution is cooled in an ice-water bath for a few minutes to maximize crystal formation. Crystals usually form as the solution temperature decreases.

Sometimes, crystals do not form in the cooled solution. In this case, two methods can be used to induce crystallization. One method involves scratching the inside of the flask with a glass stirring rod. The freshly scratched glass supplies sites for seed crystal formation. Alternatively, a seed crystal of the pure compound can be placed into the solution to promote crystal growth.

Collecting, Washing, and Drying the Crystals

Vacuum filtration is the best method for separating the crystals from the **mother liquor,** or remaining solvent. A typical vacuum filtration apparatus is shown in Figure 5 on the next page.

In vacuum filtration, a receiver flask with a sidearm, called a **filter flask**, is connected by heavy-walled vacuum tubing to a vacuum source. A Büchner funnel is fitted to the filter flask with a rubber stopper or filter adapter.

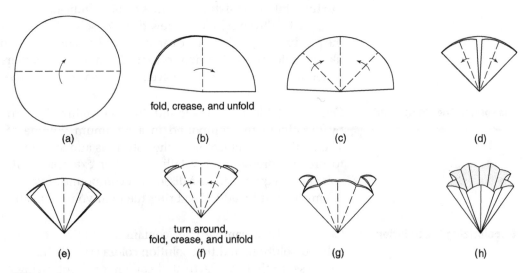

Figure 4
Folding a fluted filter paper

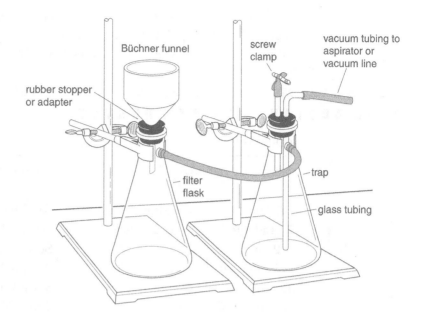

Figure 5
A typical vacuum filtration apparatus

The most common source of vacuum is a **water aspirator.** In a water aspirator, water moves past a small hole leading into a sidearm that can be attached to a trap. A partial vacuum is created because of the reduced pressure at the point where the rapidly moving water passes the hole. At that point, air is pulled into the aspirator sidearm. This phenomenon is called the **Bernoulli effect**.

A **trap** can be used in tandem with a water aspirator to prevent contamination of the solution in the filter flask with water. Sudden drops in water pressure can cause water to be drawn into the filter flask. Fitting a trap between the filter flask and the aspirator prevents any reverse water flow from reaching the filter flask.

To recover the pure crystals, the perforated Büchner funnel plate is covered with a filter paper disk, which is moistened with recrystallization solvent. With vacuum applied, the solution containing the suspended crystals is poured onto the filter paper so that a uniform thickness of crystals collects on the paper. After the mother liquor has been pulled through the filter, the crystals are washed with small portions of cold solvent. Then the crystals are dried and their mass is measured.

Calculating Percent Recovery

Percent recovery is calculated by dividing the mass of the recrystallized compound by the mass of the crude compound before recrystallization, as shown in Equation 1.

$$\% \text{ recovery} = \left(\frac{\text{mass of recrystallized compound, g}}{\text{mass of crude compound, g}}\right)(100\%) \quad (\text{Eq. 1})$$

Assessing Purity

Purity of a recrystallized compound is assessed by observing its color and by measuring its melting point range. If a compound is described in the chemical literature as having white crystals, the recrystallized compound should appear white. If the compound has an off-white color, the compound should again be recrystallized using activated carbon.

A pure compound melts over a narrow range of 1–3 °C near its reported melting point. If a *dry* recrystallized compound has a melting point range of four degrees or more, it should be recrystallized again.

PURIFYING ACETANILIDE BY RECRYSTALLIZATION

Equipment

2 beakers, 100-mL	Microspatula
250-mL beaker[†]	Pasteur pipet, with latex bulb
Büchner funnel, with filter paper	Sand bath[*]
2 graduated Erlenmeyer flasks, 25-mL	Screw clamp
	Stirring rod, glass
11-cm fluted filter paper	2 support stands
125-mL filter flask, with 1-hole stopper	5 test tubes, 13 × 100-mm
	2 utility clamps
Short-stem filter funnel	Vacuum trap
10-mL graduated cylinder	250-mL filter flask
25-mL graduated cylinder	2-hole stopper
Hot plate	2 pieces glass or plastic tubing
Labels	Vacuum tubing

[*]or crystallizing dish on electric hot plate or electric heating well with heat controller
[†]for ice bath

Reagents and Properties

Substance	Quantity	Molar mass (g/mol)	mp (°C)	bp(°C)
Acetanilide	1 g	135.17	113–115	
Acetone	2 mL	58.08		56
Carbon, activated	60 mg			
Ethanol	2 mL	46.07		78
Petroleum ether	2 mL	*		35–60

*mixture of hydrocarbons

Preview

- Check solubility of acetanilide in four solvents
- Choose a recrystallizing solvent
- Weigh the acetanilide
- Dissolve the acetanilide in the hot recrystallizing solvent
- Add activated carbon to remove dissolved impurities and filter the hot solution

- Recrystallize the pure acetanilide
- Collect the crystals of acetanilide
- Wash, dry, and weigh the crystals
- Measure the melting points of crude and recrystallized acetanilide

PROCEDURE

CAUTION

Wear departmentally approved safety goggles at all times while in the chemistry laboratory.

Always use caution in the laboratory. Many chemicals are potentially harmful. Prevent contact with your eyes, skin, and clothing. Avoid ingesting any of the reagents.

1. Choosing a Recrystallizing Solvent

CAUTION

Acetanilide is toxic and irritating. Acetone and ethanol are flammable and irritating. Petroleum ether is flammable and toxic. Use these compounds in a *fume hood*.

Label four 13 × 100-mm test tubes "acetone", "water", "ethanol", and "petroleum ether". Place approximately 100 mg of acetanilide into each test tube. Use a microspatula to pulverize the acetanilide. Place 2.0 mL of the appropriate solvent into each test tube. Thoroughly stir each mixture. Record whether the acetanilide is soluble or insoluble in each solvent at room temperature.

NOTE: Lumps of acetanilide may be slow to dissolve, interfering with the correct solvent selection.

CAUTION

Heated test tubes containing solvent boil over easily. Be careful to avoid burns from the hot solvent.

Select the test tube(s) containing the solvent(s) in which acetanilide did not dissolve at room temperature. Using a sand bath, heat the mixture(s) to boiling. Record whether acetanilide is soluble or insoluble in each hot solvent.

Allow the heated solvent(s) to cool slowly to room temperature. Prepare an ice–water bath by half filling a 250-mL beaker with equal volumes of ice and water. Place the tube(s) into the bath for 5 min, and observe whether recrystallization occurs. Record your observations.

Based on your observations, choose an appropriate solvent from which to recrystallize acetanilide. Consult your laboratory instructor concerning your solvent choice before proceeding to Part 2. Place the solvents in the test tubes into appropriate containers labeled "Recovered Acetone", "Recovered Ethanol", "Recovered Water", and "Recovered Petroleum Ether", provided by your laboratory instructor.

2. Dissolving the Compound

Weigh 500 mg of acetanilide and place it into a 25-mL Erlenmeyer flask. Place 15 mL of the appropriate recrystallizing solvent into a second 25-mL Erlenmeyer flask. Add a boiling chip. Using a hot plate, heat the solvent to boiling.

Using beaker tongs, pick up the hot flask containing the boiling solvent. Use a Pasteur pipet to add 0.5–1 mL of boiling solvent to the flask containing the acetanilide. Swirl the flask with each addition. Keep the solvent in both flasks at boiling by placing the flasks on the hot plate. Continue the solvent additions until the acetanilide *just* dissolves.

Using beaker tongs, remove the flasks from the hot plate. Allow the acetanilide solution to cool below the solvent boiling point. Observe the solution color. Record your observations. Measure and record your solvent volume.

Calculate the additional solvent volume needed to have a 5% excess. Measure and add that solvent volume to the acetanilide flask.

3. Decolorizing the Solution

CAUTION

Activated carbon is an irritant. Prevent eye, skin, and clothing contact. Avoid inhaling dust and ingesting the carbon. *Do not add carbon to a boiling solution.* This addition will cause the solution to boil over and burn your skin. Also, do not boil a solution containing carbon too vigorously, or the solution may boil over.

Assemble a gravity filtration apparatus, as shown in Figure 3 earlier in this module. Weigh 60 mg of activated carbon. *Conduct the Procedure in Parts A and B simultaneously.*

NOTE: So that crystals will not form in the funnel, plan to filter the boiling solution from Part B using the filter apparatus from Part A while the filter apparatus is still hot.

A. Heating the Gravity Filtration Apparatus

Place 20 mL of the recrystallizing solvent into a 100-mL beaker. Add a boiling chip. Heat the solvent to boiling on a hot plate. Using beaker tongs, pick up the hot beaker containing the boiling solvent. Preheat the filtration apparatus by pouring the solvent through the funnel containing a fluted filter paper. Do not allow the boiling chip to go into the funnel. Collect the solvent in another beaker. Place the gravity filtration apparatus on the hot plate to keep the solvent hot.

B. Adding the Activated Carbon

At the same time, add the 60 mg of activated carbon to the Erlenmeyer flask with the acetanilide solution. Reheat the solution to boiling.

When you have completed Parts *A* and *B*, pour the boiling solvent from the filtration apparatus beaker into the other 100-mL beaker. *While the gravity filtration apparatus is still hot from the recrystallizing solvent,* filter the boiling solution containing the carbon through the gravity filtration apparatus. Collect the liquid in the 25-mL receiving flask. Observe the color of the filtered solution. Record your observations.

4. Recrystallizing Pure Acetanilide

Allow the decolorized solution containing the acetanilide to cool to room temperature. When the solution has reached room temperature, place the Erlenmeyer flask into an ice–water bath for 5 min to complete the crystallization.

5. Collecting, Washing, and Drying the Crystals

While the solvent and solution are cooling in the ice bath, assemble a vacuum filtration apparatus as shown in Figure 5 earlier in this module, using a 125-mL filter flask. Also prepare a washing solvent by placing 5 mL of the recrystallizing solvent into a test tube. Cool the tube and its contents in the ice-water bath.

Weigh a filter paper and record its mass. Once crystallization is complete, turn on the water to the aspirator, and moisten the filter paper with a few drops of recrystallizing solvent. Swirl the flask containing the acetanilide, and pour the crystals and mother liquor into the Büchner funnel, using a glass rod to direct the crystals to the middle of the filter paper.

After the mother liquor has been pulled into the filter flask, release the vacuum by loosening the screw clamp on the trap. Remove the Büchner funnel from the filter flask and pour the mother liquor into a beaker. Tighten the screw clamp and reattach the Büchner funnel.

Use 4–5 mL portions of the mother liquor to rinse the remaining crystals of acetanilide from the Erlenmeyer flask. Pour the rinses into the Büchner funnel.

Wash the crystals in the Büchner funnel with the cold recrystallizing solvent. Allow the crystals to dry by pulling air through the funnel for 10 min. Then disconnect the vacuum tubing and turn off the aspirator. Remove the filter paper and crystals. Disassemble the filtration apparatus.

Weigh your dried crystals and filter paper, and record the mass. Observe the color and shape of the crystals and record your observations.

Measure and record the melting point ranges of both crude and recrystallized acetanilide. If your laboratory instructor directs you to do so, place your crystals into a labeled sample vial to turn in.

6. Cleaning Up

Use the labeled collection containers provided by your laboratory instructor. Clean your glassware with soap or detergent.

CAUTION

Wash your hands thoroughly with soap or detergent before leaving the laboratory.

name   section   date

Post-Laboratory Questions

1. The solubility of benzoic acid in water is 6.80 g per 100 mL at 100 °C and 0.34 g per 100 mL at 25 °C.

   (a) Calculate the minimum volume of water needed to dissolve 1.00 g of benzoic acid at 100 °C.

   (b) Calculate the maximum theoretical percent recovery from the recrystallization of 1.00 g of benzoic acid from 15 mL of water, assuming the solution is filtered at 25 °C.

2. The solubility of acetanilide in your recrystallizing solvent is 5.0 mg per mL at 10 °C.

   (a) Calculate the maximum percent recovery in this experiment, assuming a 15.0-mL recrystallizing solution is filtered at 10 °C.

   (b) Calculate the percent recovery of the acetanilide produced in your experiment.

   (c) How do your results compare to the maximum percent recovery? Briefly explain.

3. A student rushed through this experiment. Describe the effect that the following procedural changes would have on the percent recovery of acetanilide. Briefly explain the basis of each answer.

   (a) Rather than adding 0.5-mL portions of boiling solvent to the acetanilide, the student added 5-mL portions of boiling solvent.

   (b) The student did not pre-heat the gravity filtration apparatus in Part 3.

   (c) The student forgot to cool 5 mL of solvent in Part 5 and washed the crystals with room-temperature solvent.

name   section   date

Pre-Laboratory Assignment

1. Briefly explain why

   (a) you should not heat organic solvents over a Bunsen burner flame.

   (b) you should add activated carbon to a cool solution and then heat the mixture to boiling rather than add the carbon to a boiling solution.

2. Indicate a procedure to solve the following recrystallization problems.

   (a) oiling out

   (b) lack of crystal formation

   (c) presence of colored impurities

   (d) premature recrystallization in the funnel stem during gravity filtration

3. Compound *A*, a white crystalline solid with a melting point of 75 °C, has the solubility profile shown in the following table. Which of the solvents listed would be a good recrystallizing solvent for Compound *A*? Briefly explain. The boiling points for these solvents are shown in Table 1 earlier in this module.

Compound A solubility profile

Solvent	Solubility at 25 °C	Solubility at boiling point
Water	I	S
Methanol	I	S
Acetone	S	S
Ethyl ether	S	S

4. A student purified a 500-mg sample of phthalic acid by recrystallization from water. The published solubility of phthalic acid in 100 mL of water is 0.54 g at 14 °C and 18 g at 99 °C.

(a) What is the smallest volume of boiling water the student could use to dissolve 500 mg of phthalic acid?

Dissolution of phthalic acid in boiling water produced a dark-colored solution. The student allowed the solution to cool, added several spatulas full of activated carbon, and heated the mixture to boiling. After gravity filtration, the clear and colorless solution was allowed to cool to room temperature. Crystals formed, and the student isolated 380 mg of phthalic acid.

(b) Calculate the percent recovery of phthalic acid in this experiment.

(c) Suggest one or more procedural errors the student made that could be responsible for some loss of phthalic acid.

TECH **0704**

Separating Cyclohexane and Toluene by Distillation

Prepared by Jerry Manion, University of Central Arkansas

PURPOSE OF THE EXPERIMENT

Separate two miscible liquids, either by macroscale or microscale process, using simple and fractional distillation. Compare the efficiencies of simple and fractional distillation.

EXPERIMENTAL OPTIONS

Macroscale Distillation

Microscale Distillations

A. Using Glassware with Elastomeric Connectors

B. Using the Hickman Still

C. Using Test Tube Reflux

BACKGROUND REQUIRED

You should be familiar with basic laboratory techniques for measuring volumes of chemical compounds. You should know how to prepare a bent-tip Pasteur pipet for microscale distillations. You should know how to use a refractometer to measure refractive index.

BACKGROUND INFORMATION

Distillation is a technique widely used in organic chemistry for separating compounds based on differences in their boiling points. Many organic compounds are **volatile**; that is, they have relatively high vapor pressures and low boiling points. During distillation, such volatile compounds are heated to boiling in one container, called the **pot**. The vapors produced are then cooled and reliquefied by passing them through a water-cooled **condenser**, and collected in a separate container, called the **receiver**. This technique can be used to remove a volatile solvent from a nonvolatile product; to separate a volatile product from nonvolatile impurities; or to separate two or more volatile products that have sufficiently different boiling points.

When a liquid is placed in a closed container, some of the molecules evaporate into any unoccupied space in the container. **Evaporation**, which occurs at temperatures below the boiling point of a compound, involves the transition from liquid to vapor of *only* those molecules at the liquid surface. Evaporation continues until an equilibrium is reached between molecules entering and leaving the liquid and vapor states. The pressure exerted by these gaseous molecules on the walls of the container is the **equilibrium vapor pressure**. The magnitude of this vapor pressure depends on the physical characteristics of the compound and increases as temperature increases.

If the liquid is heated to its boiling point, quite a different phenomenon occurs. The **boiling point** is the temperature at which the vapor pressure of the liquid is equal to the external pressure applied to the surface of the liquid. This external pressure is commonly atmospheric pressure. At the boiling point, bubbles of vapor are produced throughout the liquid, and the vapor pressure inside the bubbles is sufficiently high to allow them to grow in size. The escape of these bubbles results in the characteristic chaotic motion of the liquid identified as **boiling**.

Liquid is converted to vapor more rapidly by boiling than by evaporation. If the heating rate is increased, the temperature of the boiling liquid does not change, but the rate at which vapor is produced from the liquid increases. This increase occurs because the energy that is supplied by the increased heating rate is absorbed as more liquid molecules overcome intermolecular interactions and enter the vapor phase.

When a mixture of two or more volatile compounds is heated, the vapor pressure of the mixture equals the sum of the vapor pressures of each compound in the mixture. The magnitude of the vapor pressure exerted by each compound is determined by the vapor pressure of that compound (P^0) and the mole fraction of that compound present in the mixture (X). For an ideal two-compound solution, the solution vapor pressure is expressed by Raoul's law, shown in Equation 1.

$$P_{\mathrm{T}} = X_1 P_1^{\,0} + X_2 P_2^{\,0} \qquad\qquad \text{(Eq. 1)}$$

In this equation, P_{T} is the total vapor pressure of the solution, $P_1^{\,0}$ is the vapor pressure of pure compound 1, X_1 is the mole fraction of compound 1, $P_2^{\,0}$ is the vapor pressure of pure compound 2, and X_2 is the mole fraction of compound 2.

When two liquids form a homogeneous solution, they are said to be **miscible**. Such a homogeneous mixture will boil at a temperature between the boiling points of the pure compounds. The exact boiling point of the mixture depends upon the relative amounts of the compounds present. Figure 1 shows the relationship between boiling point and composition for a two-compound mixture of cyclohexane and toluene.

When vapor is produced from such a liquid mixture, the composition of the vapor mixture is different from the composition of the liquid mixture from which it forms, as shown in Figure 2. The vapor contains a larger percent of the more volatile compound of the mixture, in this case cyclohexane. For example, a liquid composed of 50 percent cyclohexane

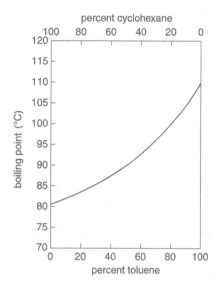

Figure 1

The boiling point of a miscible mixture is between the boiling points of the pure compounds

and 50 percent toluene would boil at 90 °C and yield a vapor composed of 70 percent cyclohexane and 30 percent toluene.

This composition change that accompanies the vaporization process is the basis for the separation of mixtures by distillation. As the vapors produced by the distillation move into the water-cooled condenser, these vapors condense to a liquid, the **distillate**, which has the same composition as the vapor from which it is formed. The distillate collected in the receiver will contain more of the more volatile compound than was present in the original mixture.

If one compound is much more volatile than the other, the compounds can be separated in one vaporization step. Such a step is called **simple distillation** and uses an apparatus that consists of only a pot, a distilling head, a condenser, an adapter, and a receiver, as shown in Figure 3.

When the boiling points of two compounds differ by less than 40 °C, they cannot be separated by simple distillation. **Fractional distillation**, a process that has the effect of many simple distillations, must be used. A fractional distillation apparatus includes a fractionating column placed

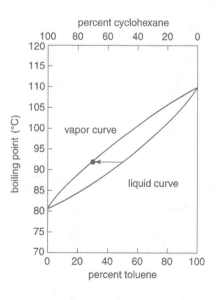

Figure 2

Vaporizing a mixture of cyclohexane and toluene produces a vapor that is enriched in cyclohexane

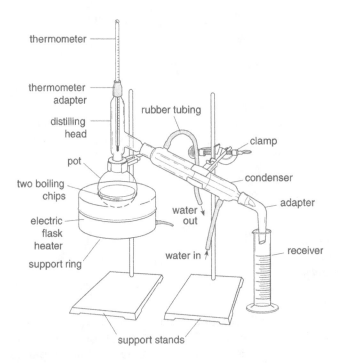

Figure 3

An apparatus for macroscale simple distillation

between the pot and the distilling head, as shown in Figure 4. Typically, any one of a variety of materials, including glass beads and metal sponge, fill the fractionating column.

The vapors generated in the pot rise up the fractionating column and encounter cooler surfaces, upon which they condense. The condensed liquid is then reheated by rising hot vapors and revaporizes. This process

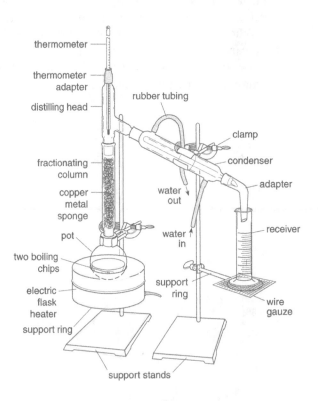

Figure 4

An apparatus for macroscale fractional distillation

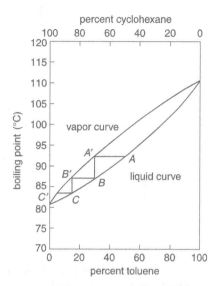

Figure 5

Each condensation and revaporization increases the concentration of the more volatile compound

of condensation and revaporization, shown graphically in Figure 5, may occur again and again as the vapors rise up the column.

Each vaporization is represented by a horizontal line connecting the liquid composition curve to the vapor composition curve. Each condensation is represented by a vertical line connecting the vapor curve to the liquid curve. For example, the 50:50 liquid mixture (*A*) vaporizes to produce a 30:70 vapor mixture (*A'*). The 30:70 vapor mixture condenses to a 30:70 liquid mixture (*B*). The 30:70 liquid mixture, in turn, vaporizes to produce a 15™:85 vapor mixture (*B'*), and so on. Each condensation–revaporization results in an increase in the concentration of the more volatile compound. These composition changes are reflected by a *decrease* in boiling temperature as the mixture moves up the fractionating column. If the condensation–revaporization is repeated a sufficient number of times, the vapors of the more volatile compound reach the top of the fractionating column in a pure form. As these vapors move into the condenser, the compound condenses and is collected as a liquid.

At the same time, the less volatile compound is enriched in the opposite direction. As the condensed liquid falls toward the pot, the pot gradually contains a higher and higher percent of the less volatile compound. Thus, a separation of the two compounds is achieved.

Each condensation and revaporization that occurs on a fractionating column is called a **theoretical plate**. A fractionating column with a large number of theoretical plates accomplishes many condensation–revaporization steps and very efficiently separates the compounds in a mixture.

The fractionating column must be positioned vertically so that condensed liquid can percolate down through the rising hot vapors. This percolation promotes equilibrium between the liquid and vapor phases, a condition that allows the column to operate at maximum efficiency and provide an optimum separation.

An equally important factor affecting separation of the compounds is the distillation rate. If the distillation is conducted too rapidly, liquid–vapor equilibria will not be established in the fractionating column, and poor separation of the compounds will result.

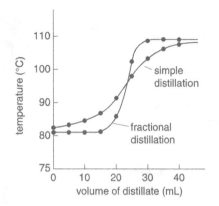

Figure 6

Distillation curves for simple and fractional distillation

As the liquid boils, a **condensation line** of vapor can be observed as it moves up the distilling head. Once these vapors reach the thermometer bulb, a dramatic temperature increase is observed. The temperature of the vapors in the distilling head provides information regarding the progress of the distillation. Initially, the vapors are rich in the more volatile compound, and the observed temperature is close to the boiling point of that compound. In a distillation with an efficient separation, the initial temperature remains relatively constant until all of that compound is collected. After the compound with the lower boiling point is completely distilled, the temperature rises sharply as the vapors of the higher-boiling compound reach the thermometer bulb. At this time, the boiling point of the higher-boiling compound is observed as it distills into the receiver.

When no fractionating column is used, or when the fractionating column is inefficient, mixtures of the distilled compounds are incompletely separated. This inefficiency is indicated by a very gradual increase in the temperature measured during the distillation. Samples collected at temperatures between the boiling points of the two compounds will consist of mixtures of the two compounds. A comparison of the results of simple and fractional distillation is shown in Figure 6.

Microscale Distillation

Distillation is a difficult organic laboratory technique to use when separating microscale volumes, because significant amounts of distillate are commonly left adhering to the glass surfaces of the apparatus. However, specialized equipment has been designed to permit the simple distillation of volumes less than one milliliter. One such apparatus, the Hickman still, is shown in Figure 10 later in this module. Another apparatus for microscale distillations uses special glassware with elastomeric connectors, as shown in Figure 8 later in this module. Microscale distillations may also be conducted in a test tube using a Pasteur pipet as a condenser and receiver.

Microscale distillations are especially useful when small volumes of a liquid must be purified for spectral or refractive index analyses. The relative amounts of cyclohexane and toluene present in a sample may be determined by measuring the refractive index of the sample. Figure 7 shows a graph that correlates the refractive index of mixtures of cyclohexane and toluene with their composition.

Refractive index measurements are typically reported at 20 °C. A refractive index measured at a temperature higher or lower than 20 °C must

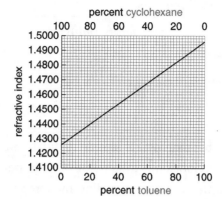

Figure 7

A correlation curve relating refractive index to the composition of cyclohexane–toluene mixtures

be corrected to 20 °C. To make this correction, Equation 2 is used, where n^{20} is the refractive index at 20 °C, n^T is the refractive index at the measured temperature, and T is the measured temperature.

$$n^{20} = n^T + 0.00045(T - 20 \text{ °C}) \qquad \text{(Eq. 2)}$$

For example, if the refractive index of a cyclohexane–toluene mixture is measured as 1.4752 at 26 °C, then the refractive index at 20 °C can be calculated:

$$n^{20} = 1.4752 + 0.00045(26 - 20 \text{ °C}) = 1.4779$$

Locating the point on the graph in Figure 7 corresponding to $n^{20} = 1.4779$ indicates that the sample contains 74 percent toluene and 26 percent cyclohexane.

Macroscale Distillation

Equipment

aluminum foil	2 support rings
boiling chips	2 support stands
copper metal sponge*	2 utility clamps
electric flask heater, with regulator	wire gauze, ceramic center*
50-mL graduated cylinder	
standard taper glassware:	
condenser, with adapter and rubber tubing	
distilling head	
fractionating column*	
100-mL round-bottom flask	
−10 to 260 °C thermometer, with adapter†	

*for fractional distillation

†adapter may be required to hold thermometer in place

Reagents and Properties

Substance	Quantity (mL)	mol mass (g/mol)	bp (°C)
cyclohexane	25	84.16	80.7
toluene	25	92.14	110.6

Preview

- Assemble macroscale simple distillation apparatus
- Place cyclohexane–toluene mixture in pot
- Distill the mixture, recording the temperature at 5-mL intervals
- Assemble macroscale fractional distillation apparatus and repeat as for simple distillation

PROCEDURE

CAUTION

Wear departmentally approved safety goggles at all times while in the chemistry laboratory.

Always use caution in the laboratory. Many chemicals are potentially harmful. Prevent contact with your eyes, skin, and clothing. Avoid ingesting any of the reagents.

General Considerations

Exercise care when assembling a distillation apparatus. Support the flask heater with a support ring attached to a support stand so that the heater can be quickly lowered away from the apparatus, if necessary.

Use a utility clamp to attach the neck of the pot to the support stand to support the apparatus in the event you remove the flask heater. Support the condenser with a second clamp and support stand.

Carefully adjust the angle of the clamp supporting the condenser. Lubricate the joints by using your finger to apply stopcock grease lightly along the interior joint section. Rotate the joint after connection to distribute the grease uniformly. Check the joints immediately before beginning the distillation, and reconnect any joints that are loose.

Select a pot size so that the pot is one-half to two-thirds full of liquid. Add two boiling chips to the pot.

NOTE: Overfilling the pot can result in bumping or foaming of material into the receiver. Boiling chips provide a surface on which vapor bubbles can form. This bubble formation helps prevent superheating and bumping of the liquid.

Insert the thermometer into a thermometer adapter so that the top of the thermometer bulb is even with or slightly below the bottom of the side arm on the distilling head, as shown in Figure 3 earlier in this module.

NOTE: Carefully positioning the thermometer ensures that the bulb is submerged in any vapors that pass through the distilling head and that the vapor temperature is measured accurately.

Use rubber tubing to attach the condenser to a water tap and to discharge water from the condenser to the drain.

NOTE: Water should enter the condenser at the bottom and exit from the top so that no air remains in the cooling jacket. A moderate flow of water is sufficient for cooling.

Place the end of the adapter inside the receiver to minimize the release of vapors into the room.

CAUTION

Heating a closed apparatus can cause the apparatus to rupture. Make certain the distillation apparatus has an opening to the atmosphere. *Do not heat a closed container.*

Discontinue the distillation before all of the liquid is gone from the pot. Some organic compounds explode when heated to dryness. *Do not distill to dryness.*

1. Conducting Simple Distillation

CAUTION

Cyclohexane is flammable and irritating. Toluene is flammable and toxic. If possible, use a *fume hood*.

Do not add boiling chips to a hot liquid. The large surface area of the boiling chip can cause the hot liquid to foam out of the apparatus and cause burns.

Assemble the simple distillation apparatus shown in Figure 3 earlier in this module, using a 100-mL round-bottom flask for the pot and a 50-mL graduated cylinder for the receiver. Place two boiling chips and 25 mL each of cyclohexane and toluene into the pot, taking care not to spill any chemicals onto the flask heater. Start the flow of water through the condenser. Check the apparatus and reconnect any joints that are loose.

Heat the mixture to boiling. Adjust the heater to produce distillate at a rate that is no greater than one drop per s. Record the temperature when you collect the first drop of distillate and again after every 5 mL of distillate you collect. Continue the distillation until the temperature reaches 110 °C or until fewer than 5 mL of liquid remains in the pot.

NOTE: As the liquid boils, watch for the condensation line of vapor as it moves up the distilling head. To observe and record an accurate temperature reading, the *entire thermometer bulb* must be immersed in vapor.

Turn off the heater and lower it away from the pot. Allow the pot to cool for a few minutes. Then turn off the water to the condenser.

2. Conducting Fractional Distillation

Cyclohexane is flammable and irritating. Toluene is flammable and toxic. If possible, use a *fume hood*.

Do not add boiling chips to a hot liquid. The large surface area of the boiling chip can cause the hot liquid to foam out of the apparatus and cause burns.

Assemble the fractional distillation apparatus shown in Figure 4 earlier in this module, using a 100-mL round-bottom flask for the pot and a 50-mL graduated cylinder for the receiver. Pack the fractionating column with copper metal sponge, as directed by your laboratory instructor.

NOTE: Be careful to position the fractionating column vertically to promote mixing of the liquid and vapor phases. The fractionating column looks much like a condenser, but has indentations in the inner jacket to support the column packing. Be careful; these indentations are easily broken. The outer jacket insulates against heat loss from the inner jacket during distillation. *Do not pass water through the fractionating column.*

Place two boiling chips and 25 mL each of cyclohexane and toluene into the pot. Start the water flow through the condenser. Check the apparatus and reconnect any joints that are loose.

Heat the mixture in the pot to boiling. Observe the condensation line as it moves up the fractionating column.

When the vapors reach the top of the column packing, reduce the heating rate so the vapor condensation line remains just above the column packing and below the side arm of the distilling head. Maintain the vapor condensation line in this position for 5 min to allow the vapor and liquid in the column to reach equilibrium.

Wrap the fractionating column and distilling head with aluminum foil to minimize the temperature fluctuations during the distillation. Then adjust the heating rate to produce distillate at a rate no greater than 1 drop per s.

Record the temperature when you collect the first drop of distillate and again after every 5 mL of distillate you collect. Continue the distillation until the temperature reaches 110 °C or until fewer than 5 mL of liquid remains in the pot.

Turn off the heater and lower it from the pot. Allow the pot to cool for a few minutes. Then turn off the water to the condenser.

3. Cleaning Up

Use the labeled collection containers provided by your laboratory instructor. Clean your glassware with soap or detergent.

Wash your hands thoroughly with soap or detergent before leaving the laboratory.

MICROSCALE DISTILLATIONS

A. Using Glassware with Elastomeric Connectors

Equipment

aluminum foil	microspatula
100-mL beaker	2 receiver vials, 5-mL, with screw caps
boiling chips	
copper metal sponge*	sand bath†
glassware with elastomeric connectors	2 support rings
	support stand
5-mL boiling flask	−10 to 260 °C thermometer, with adapter
distilling head with air condenser	
	2 utility clamps
distilling column*	wire gauze, ceramic center

*for fractional distillation
†sand in crystallizing dish on electric hot plate or sand in electric heating well with heat controller

Reagents and Properties

Substance	Quantity (mL)	mol mass (g/mol)	bp (°C)
cyclohexane	1.5	84.16	80.7
toluene	1.5	92.14	110.6

Preview

- Assemble microscale simple distillation apparatus
- Place cyclohexane-toluene mixture in pot
- Distill the mixture
- Collect the distillate, recording the temperature as a function of the number of drops
- Assemble microscale fractional distillation apparatus and repeat as for simple distillation

PROCEDURE

CAUTION

Wear departmentally approved safety goggles at all times while in the chemistry laboratory.

Always use caution in the laboratory. Many chemicals are potentially harmful. Prevent contact with your eyes, skin, and clothing. Avoid ingesting any of the reagents.

General Considerations

Exercise care when assembling a distillation apparatus. Support the flask heater with a support ring attached to a support stand so that the heater can be quickly lowered away from the apparatus, if necessary.

Use a utility clamp to attach the neck of the pot to the support stand to support the apparatus in the event you remove the flask heater.

Select a pot size so that the pot is one-half to two-thirds full of liquid. Add a boiling chip to the pot.

NOTE: Overfilling the pot can result in bumping or foaming of material into the receiver. A boiling chip provides a surface on which vapor bubbles can form. This bubble formation helps prevent superheating and bumping of the liquid.

Insert the thermometer into a thermometer adapter so that the top of the thermometer bulb is even with or slightly below the bottom of the side arm on the distilling head-condenser, as shown in Figure 8.

NOTE: Carefully positioning the thermometer ensures that the bulb is submerged in any vapors that pass through the distilling head and that the vapor temperature is measured accurately.

Place the end of the distilling head-condenser side arm inside the receiver to minimize the release of vapors into the room. Support the ice-filled beaker with wire gauze on a support ring.

CAUTION

Heating a closed apparatus can cause the apparatus to ruptur. Make certain the distillation apparatus has an opening to the atmosphere. *Do not heat a closed container.*

Discontinue the distillation before all of the liquid is gone from the pot. Some organic compounds explode when heated to dryness. *Do not distill to dryness.*

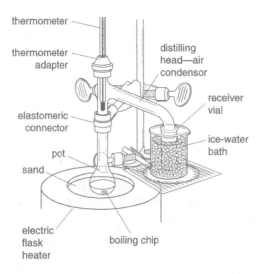

Figure 8

An apparatus using elastomeric connectors for microscale simple distillation

1. Conducting Simple Distillation

CAUTION

Cyclohexane is flammable and irritating. Toluene is flammable and toxic. If possible, use a *fume hood*.

Assemble the simple distillation apparatus as shown in Figure 8, using a 5-mL boiling flask for the pot and a 5-mL vial for the receiver. Place a boiling chip and 1.5 mL each of cyclohexane and toluene into the pot.

Position the thermometer bulb below the side arm of the distilling head–condenser, and place the end of the air condenser as deeply as possible into the receiver. Place the receiver into a 100-mL beaker and surround the receiver with ice. Check the apparatus and reconnect any joints that are loose.

Heat the mixture to boiling. Adjust the heating rate by using a spatula to move the hot sand either around or away from the pot. Control the heating rate to produce distillate at a rate of about 2–4 drops per min.

NOTE: As the liquid boils, watch for the condensation line of vapor as it moves up the distilling head. To observe and record an accurate temperature reading, the *entire thermometer bulb* must be immersed in vapor.

Read and record the temperature when you collect the first drop of distillate and again after every 5 drops of distillate you collect. Continue the distillation until the temperature remains constant at 110 °C or until the pot is almost dry. Discontinue the heating before all of the mixture distills and the pot becomes completely dry. Lower the heater away from the pot.

2. Conducting Fractional Distillation

CAUTION

Cyclohexane is flammable and irritating. Toluene is flammable and toxic. If possible, use a *fume hood*.

Assemble the fractional distillation apparatus shown in Figure 9, using a 5-mL boiling flask for the pot and a 5-mL vial for the receiver. Place a boiling chip and 1.5 mL each of cyclohexane and toluene into the pot. Tightly pack the fractionating column with copper metal sponge.

Position the thermometer bulb below the side arm of the distilling head–condenser, and place the end of the air condenser as deeply as possible into the receiver. Place the receiver into a 100-mL beaker and surround the receiver with ice. Check the apparatus and reconnect any joints that are loose.

Heat the mixture to boiling. Observe the condensation line as it moves up the fractionating column. When the vapors reach the top of the column packing, reduce the heating rate so the vapor condensation line remains just above the column packing and below the side arm of the distilling head. Maintain the vapor condensation line in this position for about 5 min to allow the vapor and liquid in the column to reach equilibrium.

Wrap the fractionating column and distilling head with aluminum foil to minimize the temperature fluctuations during the distillation. Then adjust the heating rate to produce distillate at a rate of about 2–4 drops per min.

Read and record the temperature when you collect the first drop of distillate and again after every 5 drops of distillate you collect. Continue the distillation until the temperature remains constant at 110 °C or until the

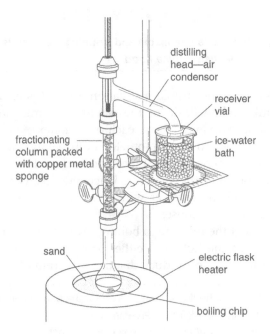

distilling
head—air
condensor

receiver
vial

fractionating
column packed
with copper metal
sponge

ice-water
bath

sand

electric flask
heater

boiling chip

Figure 9
An apparatus using elastomeric connectors for microscale fractional distillation

pot is almost dry. Discontinue the heating before the boiling flask becomes completely dry, and lower the heater away from the pot.

3. Cleaning Up

Use the labeled collection containers provided by your laboratory instructor. Clean your glassware with soap or detergent.

> **CAUTION**
>
> **Wash your hands thoroughly with soap or detergent before leaving the laboratory.**

MICROSCALE DISTILLATIONS

B. Using the Hickman Still

Equipment

boiling chips	support stand
2 conical vials, 3-mL	−10 to 150 °C thermometer,
Hickman still	small size to fit Hickman still
magnetic spinning band*	−10 to 260 °C thermometer,
microburner	for sand bath
microspatula	tongs
3 Pasteur pipets, with latex bulb	3 utility clamps
sand bath†	6 vials, 2-mL, with screw caps

*for fractional distillation

†sand in crystallizing dish on electric hot plate or sand in electric heating well with heat controller

Reagents and Properties

Substance	Quantity (mL)	mol mass (g/mol)	bp (°C)
cyclohexane	1.0	84.16	80.7
toluene	1.0	92.14	110.6

Preview

- Prepare a bent-tip Pasteur pipet
- Assemble Hickman apparatus and add cyclohexane–toluene mixture
- Conduct the distillation, collecting samples from 80–90 °C, 90–100 °C, and 100–110 °C
- Repeat the Procedure using a Teflon spinning band for fractional distillation
- Determine the percent composition of the samples, using refractive index

PROCEDURE

CAUTION

Wear departmentally approved safety goggles at all times while in the chemistry laboratory.

Always use caution in the laboratory. Many chemicals are potentially harmful. Prevent contact with your eyes, skin, and clothing. Avoid ingesting any of the reagents.

CAUTION

Cyclohexane is flammable and irritating. Toluene is flammable and toxic. If possible, use a *fume hood*.

1. Conducting a Simple Distillation

Prepare a bent-tip Pasteur pipet by heating the pipet in a microburner flame. Use tongs to bend the pipet to a 30° angle 1 cm from the tip.

NOTE: A standard Pasteur pipet can be used in a Hickman still model that has a built-in side port.

Transfer 1.0 mL each of cyclohexane and toluene into a 3-mL conical vial, and add a small boiling chip. Attach the Hickman still head and clamp the apparatus vertically in a sand bath, as shown in Figure 10.

Place a thermometer through the center opening of the still head so that the thermometer bulb is positioned as shown in Figure 10. Raise the sand-bath temperature to about 90 °C. Then gradually increase the sand-bath temperature at a rate of 2 °C per min. Collect the material that distills when the Hickman still thermometer registers 80–90 °C. Using a bent-tip Pasteur pipet, remove the distillate that condenses in the collar of the still head. Transfer the distillate to an appropriately labeled sample vial.

NOTE: Cyclohexane and toluene are quite volatile. Cap the vials to ensure that the small samples do not evaporate.

Collect a second sample that distills in the range 90–100 °C and a third sample in the range 100–110 °C.

2. Conducting Fractional Distillation

Transfer 1.0 mL each of cyclohexane and toluene into a 3-mL conical vial. Attach the Hickman still head containing a magnetic spinning band, and clamp the apparatus vertically in a sand bath, as shown in Figure 11.

Place a thermometer through the center opening of the still head so that the thermometer bulb is positioned, as shown in Figure 11. Raise the sand-bath temperature to 90 °C. When the mixture begins to boil, turn on the magnetic stirrer to a low setting to start the spinning band. Then gradually increase the sand-bath temperature at a rate of 2 °C per min. As the vapor enters the bottom of the still column, increase the spinning band rate to a middle range setting. Once liquid begins to collect in the collar of the still, increase the spinning band rate to the maximum setting.

Collect the material that distills when the Hickman still thermometer registers in the range 80–90 °C. Using a bent-tip Pasteur pipet, remove the distillate that condenses in the collar of the still head. Transfer the distillate to an appropriately labeled sample vial.

NOTE: Cyclohexane and toluene are quite volatile. Cap the vials to ensure that the small samples do not evaporate.

Collect a second sample that distills in the range 90–100 °C and a third that distills in the range 100–110 °C.

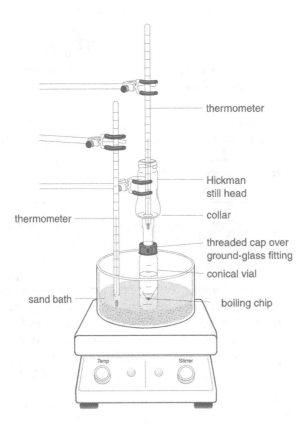

Figure 10

A Hickman still assembly for simple distillation

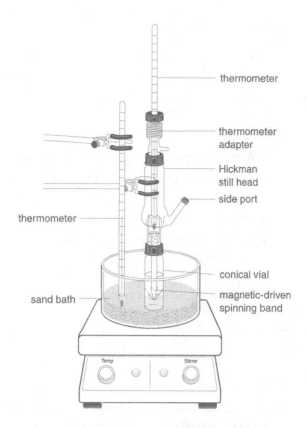

Figure 11
A Hickman still assembly for fractional distillation

3. Measuring Refractive Index

Using a refractometer, measure the refractive index of the compounds in each vial. Correct the refractive indices for temperature, using Equation 2.

Using the correlation curve shown in Figure 7 earlier in this experiment and the corrected refractive index for the solution in each collection vial, determine the percent of cyclohexane and toluene in each sample.

4. Cleaning Up

Use the labeled collection containers provided by your laboratory instructor. Clean your glassware with soap or detergent.

 CAUTION

Wash your hands thoroughly with soap or detergent before leaving the laboratory.

MICROSCALE DISTILLATIONS

C. Using Test Tube Reflux

Equipment

boiling chips	support stand
copper metal sponge*	2 test tubes, 13 × 100-mm
microspatula	−10 to 260 °C thermometer
2 Pasteur pipets, with latex bulb	utility clamp
sand bath†	6 vials, 2-mL, with screw caps

*for fractional distillation
†sand in crystallizing dish on electric hot plate or sand in electric heating well with heat controller

Reagents and Properties

Substance	Quantity (mL)	mol mass (g/mol)	bp (°C)
cyclohexane	1.0	84.16	80.7
toluene	1.0	92.14	110.6

Preview

- Assemble apparatus and add cyclohexane–toluene mixture
- Save sample of original simple distillation mixture for analysis
- Distill approximately half of the mixture
- Transfer residue to vial
- Using refractive index, analyze the composition of the original mixture, the distillate, and the pot residue
- Repeat the Procedure for fractional distillation, using a test tube packed with copper metal sponge

PROCEDURE

CAUTION

Wear departmentally approved safety goggles at all times while in the chemistry laboratory.

Always use caution in the laboratory. Many chemicals are potentially harmful. Prevent contact with your eyes, skin, and clothing. Avoid ingesting any of the reagents.

CAUTION

Cyclohexane is flammable and irritating. Toluene is flammable and toxic. If possible, use a *fume hood*.

1. Conducting Simple Distillation

Place 1.0 mL each of cyclohexane and toluene into a 13 × 100-mm test tube. Mix well and add one small boiling chip. Using a Pasteur pipet, remove about 5 drops of the mixture, and place the drops into a small vial labeled "Original Mixture–Simple".

NOTE: Cyclohexane and toluene are volatile. Cap the vials to ensure that the small samples do not evaporate.

Clamp the test tube in a vertical position. Use a sand bath to heat the liquid until the liquid boils and the condensation line for the vapor is about 2 cm from the top of the test tube, as shown in Figure 12.

Squeeze the bulb of a Pasteur pipet, place the pipet tip into the hot vapors, and *very slowly* draw the vapors into the cool pipet, where the vapors will condense. Transfer this distillate to a small vial labeled "Distillate–Simple". Repeat the process until you collect about half of the mixture in the distillate vial.

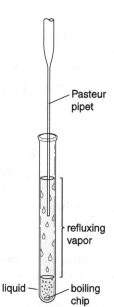

Figure 12

Simple distillation of very small samples using a test tube and a Pasteur pipet

Remove the test tube from the sand bath, allow it to cool, and transfer the remaining liquid into a vial labeled "Pot Residue–Simple".

2. Conducting Fractional Distillation

Place 1.0 mL each of cyclohexane and toluene into a 13 × 100-mm test tube, mix well, and add one small boiling chip. Using a Pasteur pipet, remove 5–10 drops of the mixture and place the drops into a small vial labeled "Original Mixture–Fractional".

Prepare a plug of copper sponge approximately 4 cm long. Tightly pack the copper plug into the test tube so that the bottom of the plug is about 1 cm above the top of the liquid and 3 cm below the mouth of the test tube, as shown in Figure 13.

Clamp the test tube in a vertical position and heat the liquid with a sand bath until the liquid boils. Observe the vapor condensation line as it moves through the copper sponge, and adjust the heat so that the condensation line reaches a point about 1 cm above the top of the copper.

Squeeze the bulb of a Pasteur pipet, place the tip into the hot vapors, and *very slowly* draw the vapors into the cool pipet, where they will

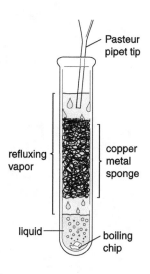

Figure 13

A test tube reflux apparatus for conducting a fractional distillation

condense. Transfer this distillate to a small vial labeled "Distillate–Fractional", and repeat the process until you collect about half of the mixture in the distillate vial.

Remove the test tube from the sand bath. Cool the test tube, remove the copper plug, and transfer the remaining liquid into a vial labeled "Pot Residue–Fractional".

3. Measuring Refractive Index

Using a refractometer, measure the refractive index of the compounds in each vial. Correct the refractive indices for temperature, using Equation 2.

Using the correlation curve shown in Figure 7 earlier in this module and the corrected refractive index for the solution in each collection vial, determine the percent of cyclohexane and toluene in each sample. Compare your results for simple and fractional distillation.

4. Cleaning Up

Use the labeled collection containers provided by your laboratory instructor. Clean your glassware with soap or detergent.

CAUTION

Wash your hands thoroughly with soap or detergent before leaving the laboratory.

_____   _____   _____
name   *section*   *date*

Post-Laboratory Questions

1. For macroscale distillations, or for microscale distillations using glassware with elastomeric connectors, plot the data for simple distillation and for fractional distillation on one graph. Plot temperature on the vertical axis and total volume of distillate on the horizontal axis, as shown in Figure 6 earlier in this module. Draw a smooth curve through the data points for each distillation.

2. (a) At what temperatures were the first drop of distillate collected in the simple and fractional distillations?

   (b) Using Figure 1, estimate the composition of these initial samples of distillate. Based on the results, what conclusion can you draw regarding the relative efficiencies of the two separations?

3. For macroscale distillations, or for microscale distillations using glassware with elastomeric connectors, compare the plot from your simple distillation with that from your fractional distillation. In which case do the changes in temperature occur more gradually? Which method is more effective in achieving separation? Briefly explain.

4. For Hickman still or for test tube microscale distillations, compare the refractive index data for simple and fractional distillations. Do the data suggest which distillation procedure is more efficient? Briefly explain.

_____   _____   _____

Pre-Laboratory Assignment

1. Briefly explain why you should not add boiling chips to a boiling liquid.

2. (a) Briefly explain how and why you should position the thermometer in the distillation head during a distillation.

(b) What is the purpose of the outer jacket on a fractionating column?

(c) How is the rate of heating adjusted when using a sand bath as a heat source?

(d) How is the distillate collected in a test tube microscale distillation?

3. What effect does an increase in the heating rate have on the boiling temperature during a distillation?

4. As molecules move up a fractional distillation column, they condense and then revaporize. During which of these steps is the concentration of the more volatile compound of the mixture increased? Briefly explain.

5. Using Figure 2, estimate the composition of a cyclohexane-toluene distillate that is collected

at 85 °C;

at 95 °C;

at 105 °C.

Separating Acids and Neutral Compounds by Solvent Extraction

Prepared by Jerry Manion, University of Central Arkansas

PURPOSE OF THE EXPERIMENT

Use solvent extraction techniques to separate a mixture consisting of a carboxylic acid, a phenol, and a neutral compound.

EXPERIMENTAL OPTIONS

Microscale Extraction
Macroscale Extraction

BACKGROUND REQUIRED

You should be familiar with the experimental techniques used to determine melting points, to test for acidity using pH paper, and to separate a solid from a solution using vacuum filtration. You should know how to speed solvent evaporation using air or nitrogen.

BACKGROUND INFORMATION

Frequently, organic chemists must separate an organic compound from a mixture of compounds, often derived from natural sources or as products of synthetic reactions. One technique used to separate the mixture compounds is called extraction. **Extraction** is a process that selectively dissolves one or more of the mixture compounds into an appropriate solvent. The solution of these dissolved compounds is often referred to as the **extract**.

Extraction processes include removal of soluble compounds from a solid matrix, such as occurs in brewing coffee or tea or in decaffeinating coffee with liquid carbon dioxide. In the organic chemistry laboratory,

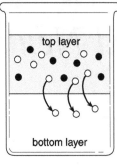

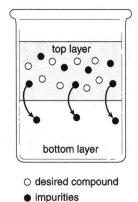

○ desired compound
● impurities

○ desired compound
● impurities

Figure 1
Extraction occurs when the desired compound changes layers, leaving impurities behind

Figure 2
Washing occurs when impurities change layers, leaving the desired compound behind

however, extraction almost always refers to the transfer of compounds from one liquid solvent to another liquid solvent.

A compound can be separated from impurities in a solution by extracting the compound from the original or first solvent into a second solvent. The compound must be more soluble in the second solvent than in the first solvent, and the impurities must be insoluble in the second solvent.

Also, to effect the extraction, the two solvents selected must be **immiscible**, or not soluble in one another, so that they produce two separate solvent layers. After dissolving the mixture in the first solvent, the solution is added to the second solvent. The two layers are vigorously mixed to maximize the surface area between them. This mixing facilitates the transfer of a dissolved compound from one layer to another. Once the transfer process is complete, the layers are again allowed to form, as shown in Figure 1. Separation of the two layers then completes the separation of the desired compound from the impurities.

Washing is the reverse process, in which the impurities are removed to the second solvent, leaving the desired compound in the original solvent, as shown in Figure 2.

Selecting the Appropriate Scale

The amount of compound to be extracted determines whether macroscale or microscale techniques should be employed for the extraction. The chemical principles associated with the extractions are identical, but the techniques are somewhat different.

Extractions using larger quantities of solvents, tens or hundreds of milliliters, require a separatory funnel, as shown in Figure 3. The solvent layers are mixed by shaking the separatory funnel. Then the layers are allowed to reform. The bottom layer is drained through the stopcock; the top layer is poured from the top of the separatory funnel.

Microscale extractions can be conducted using a test tube or a centrifuge tube. Mixing and separating the layers can be done using a Pasteur pipet.

Choosing Solvents

The first requirement in the extraction process is to select two immiscible solvents. One solvent, usually water, should be polar in nature. The second solvent should be nonpolar and might be a hydrocarbon, an ether, or a

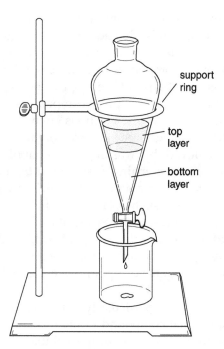

Figure 3

A separatory funnel used for macroscale extractions

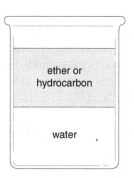

Figure 4

Ethers and hydrocarbons are less dense than water

Figure 5

Dichloromethane is more dense than water

chlorinated solvent, such as dichloromethane. When the two immiscible solvents are placed into a container, two liquid layers result. The more dense solvent is always the bottom layer.

It is important to identify the solvent in each layer. Hydrocarbons and ethers are *less dense* than water or the dilute aqueous solutions used in extractions. When one of these nonpolar solvents is used, the *water* layer is the *bottom* layer, as shown in Figure 4.

However, dichloromethane is more dense than water. When dichloromethane is used as the nonpolar solvent, the *water* layer will be the *top* layer, as shown in Figure 5.

Although the identity of each layer can be established from the density of each solvent, their identities should be confirmed. To confirm the identities of the layers, one or two drops of water are introduced *just below the surface of the top layer*. If the drops of water mix with the top layer, then the top layer is the water layer. If the drops of water fall through the top layer to the layer below, then the water layer is the bottom one. *It is a good practice to save all layers in labeled containers until the experiment is complete and the desired product is isolated.*

Often the two solvents will not completely separate after shaking, due to the formation of an emulsion at the interface between them. An **emulsion** is a suspension of small droplets of one liquid in another liquid. Emulsions are generally opaque or cloudy in appearance and are often mistaken as a third layer.

The small size of the droplets in an emulsion causes the separation of the two solvents to take place very slowly. Several procedures may be helpful to facilitate this separation. For example, gentle swirling of the container, addition of a few drops of saturated aqueous sodium chloride (NaCl) or ethanol, or addition of more solvent to dilute the solutions may help. In particularly difficult cases, it may be necessary to filter the mixture to remove small solid particles that promote emulsion formation.

A simple, but useful, guide to solubility is *like dissolves like*. That is, nonpolar compounds, including most organic compounds, are more soluble in nonpolar solvents than in polar solvents. On the other hand, ionic and polar compounds are more soluble in polar solvents, such as water. These solubility differences can be exploited to separate nonpolar compounds from ionic or polar compounds.

For example, synthetic reactions often produce ionic, inorganic salts as by-products of the desired nonpolar organic product. In such cases, these salts are removed by washing the nonpolar solvent with water. The organic compound remains dissolved in the nonpolar solvent.

Some organic compounds are sufficiently polar to be quite soluble in water. Extraction of such polar compounds into a nonpolar solvent is often difficult. The process can be facilitated by using the technique called **salting out**. Inorganic salts, such as NaCl, are dissolved in water to reduce the solubility of the organic compound in the aqueous layer. Under these conditions, the organic compound preferentially dissolves in the nonpolar layer.

Extraction is a particularly effective means of separating organic compounds if one compound in the mixture can be chemically converted to an ionic form. The ionic form is soluble in an aqueous layer and can be extracted into it. Other non-ionized organic compounds in the mixture will remain dissolved in the nonpolar solvent layer. Separation of the two layers results in the separation of the dissolved compounds.

Ionic forms of some organic compounds can be produced by reacting them with aqueous acids or bases (see Figure 6 below). Reacting organic acids with bases such as sodium hydroxide (NaOH) converts these acids to water-soluble anions. Reacting basic amines with dilute aqueous acid solutions such as hydrochloric acid (HCl) converts the amines to water-soluble cations.

The extent to which an acid-base reaction proceeds to completion depends upon the relative acidity and basicity of the reactants and products. Reactions occur so that stronger acids and bases react to produce weaker conjugate bases and acids. Recall that the pK_a is a measure of the acidity of an acid, as shown in Equation 1.

$$pK_a = -\log K_a \qquad \text{(Eq. 1)}$$

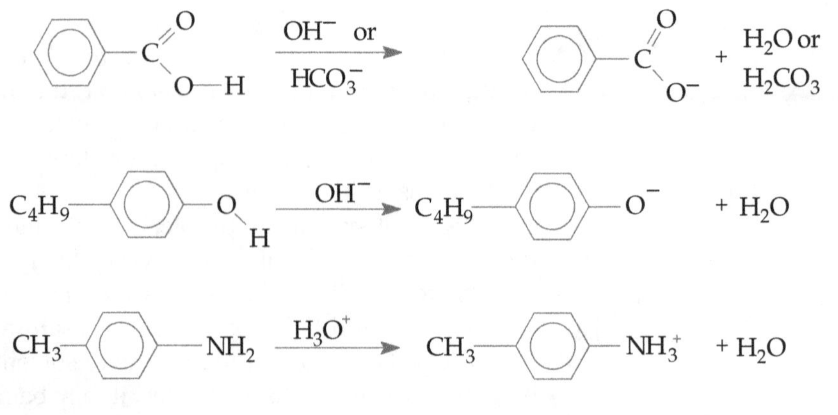

Figure 6

Organic compounds can be converted to ionic forms by reactions with aqueous solutions of acid or base

Stronger acids have smaller pK_as and their conjugate bases are inherently weaker. The position of an acid–base equilibrium can then be predicted from a knowledge of the pK_as of the acids involved. Stronger acids, those with a smaller pK_a, will react with the conjugate bases of weaker acids, those with a larger pK_a.

An analysis of Figure 7 indicates that aqueous NaOH can be used to extract both *p*-toluic acid and *p-tert*-butylphenol from a nonpolar solvent, as shown in Equations 2 and 3. The stronger base, OH⁻, removes a hydrogen ion, H⁺, from *p*-toluic acid to form the salt, *p*-toluate. The polar salt is soluble in aqueous solution. Both OH⁻ and *p*-toluate are bases. The pK_a of 16 indicates that OH⁻ is a stronger base than *p*-toluate, with a pK_a of 4.2. The stronger base takes H⁺ from the weaker base.

Similarly, OH⁻ is a stronger base than *p-tert*-butylphenoxide ion, with a pK_a of 10.2. So OH⁻ takes H⁺ from *p-tert*-butylphenol to form the water soluble *p-tert*-butylphenoxide ion.

Sodium hydrogen carbonate (NaHCO₃), with a pK_a of 6.4, is a weaker base than *p-tert*-butylphenoxide ion, so HCO₃⁻ will not take H⁺ from *p-tert*-butylphenol, as shown in Equation 4. As a result, *p-tert*-butylphenol is not converted to a salt in aqueous sodium hydrogen carbonate and does not become water soluble.

Although aqueous NaHCO₃ is not sufficiently basic to react with *p-tert*-butylphenol, NaHCO₃ will react with *p*-toluic acid to form the water soluble *p*-toluate, as shown in Equation 5.

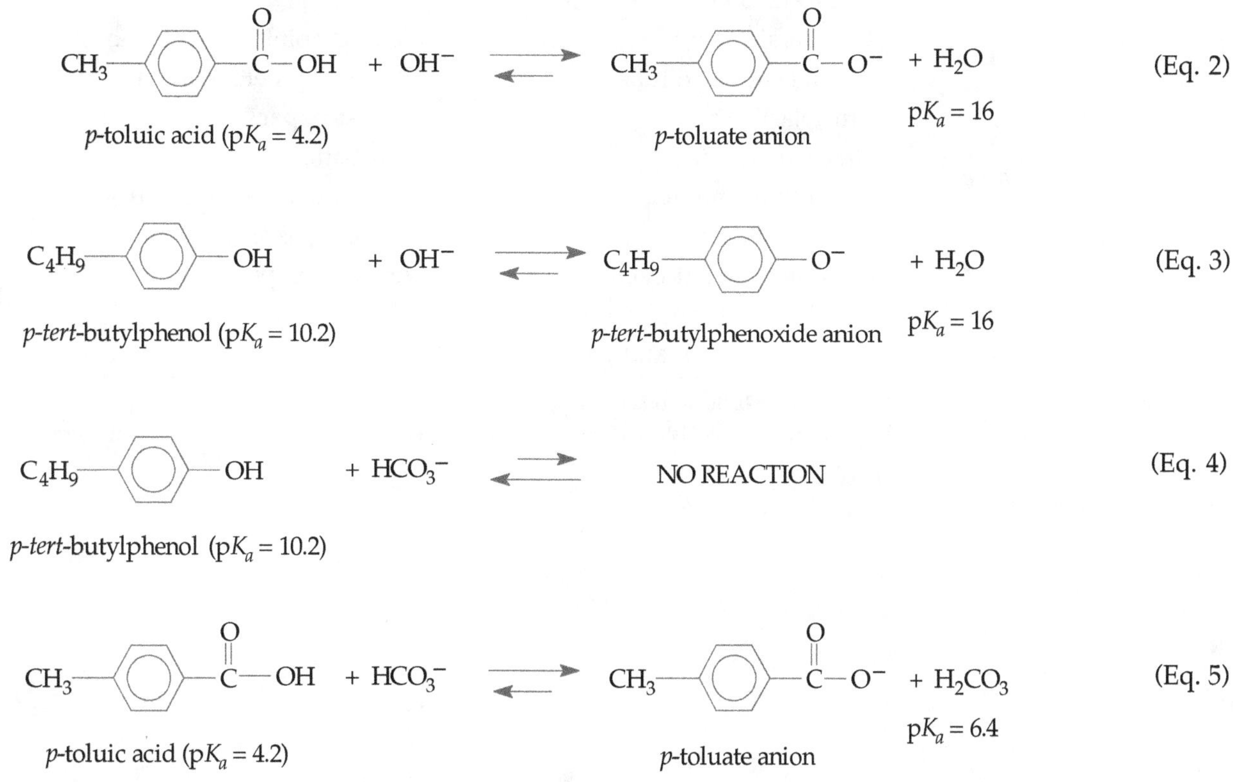

CH₃——⟨benzene ring⟩——C(=O)—OH   +   OH⁻   ⇌   CH₃——⟨benzene ring⟩——C(=O)—O⁻   +   H₂O   (Eq. 2)

p-toluic acid (pK_a = 4.2)   *p*-toluate anion   pK_a = 16

C₄H₉——⟨benzene ring⟩——OH   +   OH⁻   ⇌   C₄H₉——⟨benzene ring⟩——O⁻   +   H₂O   (Eq. 3)

p-tert-butylphenol (pK_a = 10.2)   *p-tert*-butylphenoxide anion   pK_a = 16

C₄H₉——⟨benzene ring⟩——OH   +   HCO₃⁻   ⇌   NO REACTION   (Eq. 4)

p-tert-butylphenol (pK_a = 10.2)

CH₃——⟨benzene ring⟩——C(=O)—OH   +   HCO₃⁻   ⇌   CH₃——⟨benzene ring⟩——C(=O)—O⁻   +   H₂CO₃   (Eq. 5)

p-toluic acid (pK_a = 4.2)   *p*-toluate anion   pK_a = 6.4

Figure 7

The position of an acid–base equilibrium is determined by the relative acidity of the reactant acid and the product acid

The p-toluic acid and the p-tert-butylphenol can be recovered by adding HCl to the aqueous solutions. The p-toluate and p-tert-butylphenoxide ions are stronger bases than is Cl⁻, so each one takes H⁺ from HCl. The acid forms are not water soluble, so they precipitate from solution.

The procedure you will use in this experiment exploits the differences in these reactions to separate p-toluic acid and p-tert-butylphenol from the nonpolar solvent in which they are dissolved. First, you will extract only p-toluic acid into $NaHCO_3$ solution. Then, you will extract p-tert-butylphenol into NaOH solution. Next, you will add HCl to each of the extracts to precipitate the water-insoluble p-toluic acid and p-tert-butylphenol. You will isolate the precipitates from the solutions by vacuum filtration, then air dry them. A flowchart for the separations is shown in Figure 8 on the next page.

A third compound, acetanilide, does not react with either NaOH or $NaHCO_3$ and remains dissolved in the nonpolar solvent. To recover acetanilide, you will dry the nonpolar layer with anhydrous sodium sulfate (Na_2SO_4) and evaporate the solvent in a fume hood. You will recrystallize the acetanilide in an ice bath.

After you dry the compounds, you will measure the mass of each isolated compound. Finally, you will measure the melting point of each compound and assess its purity by comparing the experimentally measured melting point with the literature value.

Microscale Extraction

Equipment

3 beakers, 50-mL	hot plate
2 beakers, 250-mL*	melting point capillary tubes
15-mL centrifuge tube,	5 Pasteur pipets, with latex bulb
with plastic cap	pH test paper
filter paper, to fit	sand bath†
Hirsch filter funnel	thermometer, −10 to 110 °C
glass stirring rod	2 watch glasses
10-mL graduated cylinder	weighing paper
Hirsch filter funnel, with	
50-mL filter flask and gasket	

*one for the ice bath, the other to support the centrifuge tube
†sand in crystallizing dish on electric hot plate or sand in electric heating well with heat controller

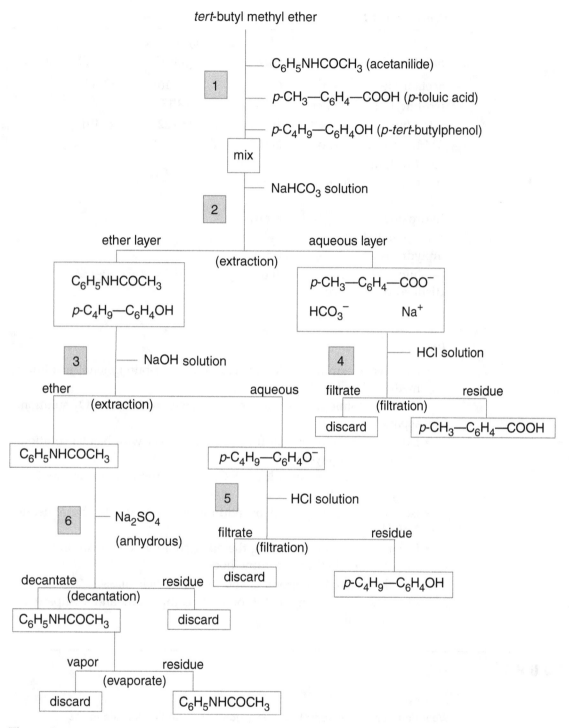

Figure 8

Flowchart for separations using microscale techniques

Reagents and Properties

Substance	Quantity	Molar mass (g/mol)	mp (°C)	bp (°C)
acetanilide	60 mg	135.16	113–115	
tert-butyl methyl ether	5 mL	88.15		55–56
p-tert-butylphenol	100 mg	150.22	98–101	
3M hydrochloric acid	2mL			
0.5M sodium hydrogen carbonate	6 mL			
0.5M sodium hydroxide	6 mL			
sodium sulfate, anhydrous	0.5 g			
p-toluic acid water, distilled or deionized	100 mg	136.15	180–182	

Preview

- Dissolve acetanilide, *p*-toluic acid, and *p-tert*-butylphenol in *t*-butyl methyl ether (see Figure 8)
- Extract *p*-toluic acid from the ether layer with NaHCO$_3$ solution, separating the layers
- Extract *p-tert*-butylphenol from the ether layer with NaOH solution, separating the layers
- Isolate *p*-toluic acid by adding HCl solution to the aqueous NaHCO$_3$ layer
- Isolate *p-tert*-butylphenol by adding HCl solution to the aqueous NaOH layer
- Isolate acetanilide by drying the ether solution, then evaporating *t*-butyl methyl ether in a fume hood
- Dry the isolated compounds and measure their masses
- Measure the melting point of each compound, and compare to literature value

PROCEDURE

CAUTION

Wear departmentally approved safety goggles at all times while in the chemistry laboratory.

Always use caution in the laboratory. Many chemicals are potentially harmful. Prevent contact with your eyes, skin, and clothing. Avoid ingesting any of the reagents.

1. Preparing the Extraction Mixture

CAUTION

Acetanilide is toxic and irritating. *tert*-Butyl methyl ether is flammable and irritating.

Weigh 50–70 mg of acetanilide and 80–120 mg each of *p*-toluic acid and *p-tert*-butylphenol. Record the exact mass of each solid. Place 5 mL of *tert*-butyl methyl ether into a 15-mL centrifuge tube. Add the three solids to the *tert*-butyl methyl ether in the centrifuge tube and mix to dissolve.

2. Extracting *p*-Toluic Acid

CAUTION

Reactions between sodium hydrogen carbonate (NaHCO$_3$) and acids produce carbon dioxide (CO$_2$) gas, which can result in foaming.

Add 2 mL of 0.5*M* aqueous NaHCO$_3$ to the ether solution in the centrifuge tube. Gently and thoroughly mix the two layers in the centrifuge tube.

NOTE: To ensure complete reaction, it is important to mix the layers well. If you are using a centrifuge tube with a tightly fitted cap that does not leak, vigorous shaking can achieve this mixing. An alternative technique is to repeatedly draw the mixture into a Pasteur pipet and then to forcefully discharge the mixture back into the tube.

Once any initial reaction has subsided, place the plastic cap on the centrifuge tube and shake gently. Remove the cap to allow any CO$_2$ gas to escape. Repeat this process several times, gradually increasing the intensity with which you shake the tube. Shake vigorously, because thorough mixing of the layers is essential.

Support the centrifuge tube in a beaker or flask and allow the liquid layers to separate. Confirm the identity of the layers by using a Pasteur pipet to introduce one or two drops of water *just below* the surface of the top layer. Make certain no air is in the pipet tip. Closely observe what happens to the drops.

Using a Pasteur pipet, carefully remove the aqueous layer and transfer it to a labeled 50-mL beaker.

To remove any toluic acid remaining in the ether layer, add a second 2-mL NaHCO$_3$ portion to the tube containing the ether mixture. Shake the tube vigorously. Remove the aqueous layer and combine it in the beaker with the first extract. Repeat with a third 2-mL NaHCO$_3$ portion.

Add 1 mL of distilled or deionized water to the centrifuge tube and mix. Remove the aqueous layer and combine it with the three NaHCO$_3$ solution extracts in the 50-mL beaker. Save this aqueous solution for Part 4.

3. Extracting *p-tert*-Butylphenol

CAUTION

0.5*M* Sodium hydroxide (NaOH) is toxic and corrosive.

Add 2 mL of 0.5*M* NaOH to the ether solution remaining in the centrifuge tube. Shake the tube vigorously.

Using a Pasteur pipet, remove the aqueous layer and transfer the layer into a clean, labeled, 50-mL beaker. Repeat the extraction of the ether layer with a second 2-mL NaOH portion. Remove the second NaOH layer and combine it with the first. Repeat with a third 2-mL NaOH portion.

Add 1 mL of water to the ether remaining in the centrifuge tube and mix. Remove the aqueous layer and combine it with the three NaOH extracts.

Save the NaOH extracts in the 50-mL beaker for Part 5. Save the ether layer remaining in the centrifuge tube for Part 6.

4. Isolating *p*-Toluic Acid

$3M$ hydrochloric acid (HCl) is toxic. Adding $3M$ HCl to the NaHCO$_3$ solution will produce CO$_2$, causing a large amount of foaming.

Select the 50-mL beaker containing the NaHCO$_3$ extracts from Part 2. Add $3M$ HCl dropwise to the NaHCO$_3$ solution to precipitate the *p*-toluic acid. Notice that foaming occurs and a precipitate of *p*-toluic acid forms. Continue to add the $3M$ HCl, dropwise with stirring, until no more solid is produced and the solution tests acidic (pH $\leq$ 3).

NOTE: To test for acidity, remove a drop of the solution with a stirring rod and place the drop on a small piece of pH test paper.

Weigh a filter paper and record its mass. Using the weighed filter paper, separate the crystals from the solution using vacuum filtration with a Hirsch funnel. Support the crystals and paper on a watch glass and allow the crystals to air dry.

5. Isolating *p-tert*-Butylphenol

Select the 50-mL beaker containing the NaOH extracts from Part 3. To remove any remaining traces of *tert*-butyl methyl ether that might inhibit the crystallization of the phenol, heat the NaOH solution to about 60 °C on a hot plate in a **fume hood**. Remove the beaker from the hot plate and allow the solution to cool.

To precipitate *p-tert*-butylphenol, add $3M$ HCl dropwise to the cooled solution until it tests acidic. If the phenol separates as an oil, cool the mixture in an ice bath to facilitate crystallization.

Weigh a filter paper and record its mass. Using the weighed filter paper, separate the *p-tert*-butylphenol crystals from the solution by filtration with a Hirsch funnel. Support the crystals and paper on a watch glass and allow the crystals to air dry.

6. Isolating Acetanilide

Anhydrous sodium sulfate (Na$_2$SO$_4$) is irritating and hygroscopic.

Select the centrifuge tube containing the ether layer from Part 3. Add approximately 0.5 g of anhydrous Na$_2$SO$_4$ to the centrifuge tube to remove any traces of water from the ether–acetanilide solution. Cap the tube, shake it, and allow it to stand for 5 min.

NOTE: After anhydrous Na$_2$SO$_4$ adsorbs water, it will look like salt or sugar.

Weigh a 50-mL beaker and record its mass. Decant the dried ether–acetanilide solution into the 50-mL beaker, leaving the Na$_2$SO$_4$ in the centrifuge tube.

Evaporate the ether, in a **fume hood**, by warming the beaker on a 50 °C sand bath while *gently* blowing air or nitrogen over the solution. Avoid overheating.

NOTE: Too much heat causes acetanilide to sublime. When the ether has evaporated, a small amount of oil will remain, and the container will feel hot to the touch.

Crystallize the oil residue, the acetanilide, by cooling the beaker in an ice bath. If necessary, scratch the bottom of the beaker with a glass stirring rod, or add a seed crystal, to induce crystallization. Allow the acetanilide crystals to dry.

7. Measuring Product Mass and Melting Point

When all of the samples are dry, measure the mass of each compound. Measure the melting point of each compound, and assess its purity by comparing the measured melting point with the literature value.

8. Cleaning Up

Use the labeled collection containers provided by your laboratory instructor. Clean your glassware with soap or detergent.

> **CAUTION**
>
> **Wash your hands thoroughly with soap or detergent before leaving the laboratory.**

Macroscale Extraction

Equipment

4 beakers, 100-mL	melting point capillary tubes
400-mL beaker, with ice	2 Pasteur pipets, with latex bulb
5.5-cm Büchner funnel	pH test paper
125-mL Erlenmeyer flask	125-mL separatory funnel
250-mL filter flask*	support ring
filter paper to fit Büchner funnel	support stand
glass stirring rod	thermometer, −10 to 110 °C
25-mL graduated cylinder	2 watch glasses
hot plate	weighing paper

*with gasket or other adapter

Reagents and Properties

Substance	Quantity	Molar mass (g/mol)	mp (°C)	bp (°C)
acetanilide	0.3 g	135.16	113–115	
tert-butyl methyl ether	25 mL	88.15		55–56
p-tert-butylphenol	0.5 g	150.22	98–101	
3M hydrochloric acid	2 mL			
0.5M sodium hydrogen carbonate	6 mL			
0.5M sodium hydroxide	6 mL			
sodium sulfate, anhydrous	1 g			
p-toluic acid	0.5 g	136.15	180–182	
water, distilled or deionized				

Preview

- Dissolve acetanilide, *p*-toluic acid, and *p-tert*-butylphenol in *t*-butyl methyl ether (See Figure 8 earlier in this module)
- Extract *p*-toluic acid from the ether layer with $NaHCO_3$ solution, separating the layers
- Extract *p-tert*-butylphenol from the ether layer with NaOH solution, separating the layers
- Isolate *p*-toluic acid by adding HCl solution to the aqueous $NaHCO_3$ layer
- Isolate *p-tert*-butylphenol by adding HCl solution to the aqueous NaOH layer
- Isolate acetanilide by drying the ether solution, then evaporating *t*-butyl methyl ether in a fume hood
- Dry the isolated compounds and measure their masses
- Measure the melting point of each compound and compare to literature value

PROCEDURE

CAUTION

Wear departmentally approved safety goggles at all times while in the chemistry laboratory.

Always use caution in the laboratory. Many chemicals are potentially harmful. Prevent contact with your eyes, skin, and clothing. Avoid ingesting any of the reagents.

1. Preparing the Extraction Mixture

CAUTION

Acetanilide is toxic and irritating. *tert*-Butyl methyl ether is flammable and irritating.

Weigh 0.25–0.35 g of acetanilide and 0.4–0.6 g each of *p*-toluic acid and *p-tert*-butylphenol. Record the exact mass of each compound. Place 25 mL of *tert*-butyl methyl ether into a 100-mL beaker. Add the three solids to the *tert*-butyl methyl ether and mix to dissolve. Pour this solution into a 125-mL separatory funnel supported by a support ring, as shown in Figure 3 earlier in this module.

NOTE: Be sure to close the stopcock at the bottom of the separatory funnel before adding solutions.

2. Extracting *p*-Toluic Acid

CAUTION

Reaction of sodium hydrogen carbonate ($NaHCO_3$) with acids produces carbon dioxide (CO_2) gas, which can result in foaming.

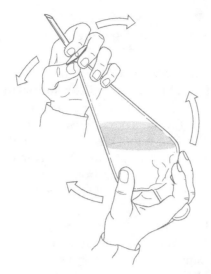

Figure 9

Mixing solutions in a separatory funnel

Add 10 mL of 0.5M aqueous $NaHCO_3$ to the ether solution in the separatory funnel. Place the glass stopper in the top of the separatory funnel, and invert the funnel while holding the stopper in place, as shown in Figure 9. Gently mix the two layers by rocking the separatory funnel back and forth.

With the funnel inverted, open the stopcock to vent any gas that is generated. Listen for the gas as it exits through the stopcock. Continue this mixing process, gradually increasing the force of the mixing, until the funnel can be shaken quite vigorously with no gas being produced upon venting. Place the funnel in the support ring and allow the layers to separate.

Confirm the identity of the layers by using a Pasteur pipet to introduce one or two drops of water *just below* the surface of the top layer. Make certain no air is in the pipet tip. Closely observe what happens to the drops.

Remove the glass stopper from the top of the funnel, and open the stopcock to allow the aqueous layer to drain into a clean, labeled 100-mL beaker. When the interface between the layers *just* reaches the bottom of the funnel (top of the stopcock), close the stopcock to retain the ether layer in the funnel.

NOTE: If you open the stopcock while the glass stopper is in the top of the separatory funnel, a slight vacuum will be created, and the bottom layer will not drain from the funnel.

 Add a second 10-mL $NaHCO_3$ portion to the funnel to remove any *p*-toluic acid remaining in the ether layer. Mix with frequent venting. After the layers have separated, drain the aqueous layer into the beaker with the first extract. Repeat with a third 10-mL $NaHCO_3$ portion.

Add 5 mL of distilled or deionized water to the separatory funnel and mix. Drain the water layer into the beaker containing the three $NaHCO_3$ solution extracts. Save this aqueous solution for Part 4.

3. Extracting *p-tert*-Butylphenol

CAUTION

0.5*M* Sodium hydroxide (NaOH) is toxic and corrosive.

Add 10 mL of 0.5*M* NaOH to the ether solution remaining in the separatory funnel. Mix the layers as before so that the NaOH and the *p-tert*-butylphenol can react. Remember to mix cautiously at first with frequent venting through the stopcock. Allow the layers to separate, and drain the aqueous NaOH layer into a clean, labeled 100-mL beaker.

Repeat the extraction of the ether layer with a second 10-mL NaOH portion. Drain the NaOH layer from the separatory funnel into the 100-mL beaker containing the first NaOH extract. Repeat with a third 10-mL NaOH portion.

Add 5 mL of water to the ether remaining in the separatory funnel and mix. Allow the layers to separate. Drain the water layer into the 100-mL beaker containing the three NaOH extracts.

Save the NaOH extracts for Part 5. Save the ether layer remaining in the separatory funnel for Part 6.

4. Isolating *p*-Toluic Acid

CAUTION

3*M* Hydrochloric acid (HCl) is toxic. Adding 3*M* HCl to the NaHCO$_3$ solution will produce CO$_2$, causing a large amount of foaming.

Select the 100-mL beaker containing the NaHCO$_3$ extracts from Part 2. To precipitate the *p*-toluic acid, carefully add 3*M* HCl to the NaHCO$_3$ solution. Notice that foaming occurs, and a precipitate of *p*-toluic acid forms. Continue to add the 3*M* HCl, dropwise with stirring, until no more solid is produced and the solution tests acidic (pH $\leq$ 3).

NOTE: To test for acidity, remove a drop of the solution with a stirring rod and place the drop on a small piece of pH test paper.

Weigh a filter paper and record its mass. Using the weighed filter paper, separate the crystals from the solution using vacuum filtration with a Büchner funnel. Support the crystals and paper on a watch glass and allow the crystals to air dry.

5. Isolating *p-tert*-Butylphenol

Select the 100-mL beaker containing the NaOH extracts from Part 3. To remove any remaining traces of *tert*-butyl methyl ether that might inhibit the crystallization of the phenol, heat the NaOH solution to about 60 °C on a hot plate in a *fume hood*. Remove the beaker from the hot plate and allow the solution to cool.

To precipitate crystals of *p-tert*-butylphenol, carefully add 3*M* HCl to the cooled solution until it is acidic. If the phenol separates as an oil, cool the mixture in an ice bath to facilitate crystallization.

Weigh a filter paper and record its mass. Using the weighed filter paper, separate the *p-tert*-butylphenol crystals from the solution by filtration with a Büchner funnel. Support the crystals and paper on a watch glass and allow the crystals to air dry.

6. Isolating Acetanilide

Anhydrous sodium sulfate (Na$_2$SO$_4$) is irritating and hygroscopic.

Select the separatory funnel containing the ether layer from Part 3. Transfer the ether–acetanilide solution from the separatory funnel to a clean 125-mL Erlenmeyer flask. Add approximately 1 g of anhydrous Na$_2$SO$_4$ to the flask to remove any traces of water from the solution. Stopper the flask and allow it to stand for 5 min with occasional swirling.

NOTE: After anyhydrous Na$_2$SO$_4$ adsorbs water, it will look like salt or sugar.

Weigh a 100-mL beaker and record its mass. Decant the clear, dried ether–acetanilide solution into the 100-mL beaker.

Evaporate the ether, in a *fume hood*, by warming the beaker on a hot plate while a stream of air passes over the solution. Avoid overheating.

NOTE: Too much heat causes acetanilide to sublime. When the ether has evaporated, a small amount of oil will remain, and the container will feel hot to the touch.

Crystallize the oil residue, the acetanilide, by cooling the beaker in an ice bath. If necessary, scratch the bottom of the beaker with a glass stirring rod, or add a seed crystal, to induce crystallization. Allow the acetanilide crystals to dry.

7. Measuring Product Mass and Melting Point

When all of the samples are dry, measure the mass of each compound. Measure the melting point of each compound, and assess its purity by comparing the measured melting point with the literature value.

8. Cleaning Up

Use the labeled collection containers provided by your laboratory instructor. Clean your glassware with soap or detergent.

Wash your hands thoroughly with soap or detergent before leaving the laboratory.

_____   _____   _____
name   *section*   *date*

Post-Laboratory Questions

1. Calculate the percent recovery of each of the compounds recovered from the original mixture.

2. If you mistakenly extracted the ether solution first with NaOH solution and then with $NaHCO_3$ solution, no crystals would be produced upon acidification of the $NaHCO_3$ layer. Briefly explain.

3. What product would you obtain if you evaporated the water from the NaOH layer prior to acidifying the layer?

4. Suppose that you used dichloromethane instead of *tert*-butyl methyl ether as the nonpolar solvent in this experiment. What changes in the procedure would you make in view of the fact that dichloromethane is more dense than water?

5. Benzoic acid (C_6H_5–COOH) is a weak acid (pK_a = 4.2) and naphthalene is neutral, neither acidic or basic. Prepare a flowchart for the separation and recovery of benzoic acid and naphthalene.

	Molar mass (g/mol)	mp (°C)	bp (°C)	pK_a
benzoic acid	122.12	122.4	249.2	4.2
naphthalene	128.16	80.2	217.9	neutral

6. After comparing the melting points of each of your compounds to their respective literature values, comment on the purity of each compound.

_____   _____   _____
name   *section*   *date*

Pre-Laboratory Assignment

1. Briefly describe the hazards you should be aware of when you work with:

(a) *tert*-butyl methyl ether

(b) 3*M* HCl

2. Briefly explain or describe the following:

(a) What is the difference between extraction and washing?

(b) How would you determine which layer is the aqueous layer after you add $NaHCO_3$ solution to the ether solution of your compounds?

(c) Why is the NaOH extract heated before acidification?

(d) What two visible evidences of reaction will you see when you acidify the $NaHCO_3$ extract with HCl solution?

(e) In which layer would *p*-toluic acid be more soluble if *p*-toluic acid were added to a two-layer mixture of *tert*-butyl methyl ether and water?

(f) How would the results differ if you added sodium *p*-toluate instead of *p*-toluic acid to the two-layer mixture of *tert*-butyl methyl ether and water?

3. Briefly explain how you will isolate *p-tert*-butylphenol after you have extracted it into NaOH solution.

4. Write the equation for the chemical reaction that will occur for the organic compound when you perform the following steps in this experiment.

(a) Add HCl solution to the $NaHCO_3$ extract.

(b) Add HCl solution to the NaOH extract.

REAC 0472

Qualitative Tests for Alkenes

Prepared by Robert G. Silberman, SUNY Cortland

PURPOSE OF THE EXPERIMENT

Use pyridinium bromide perbromide (PBP) and potassium permanganate to distinguish alkenes from alkanes and aromatic compounds. Test seven known and two unknown compounds for unsaturation.

BACKGROUND INFORMATION

Alkanes, alkenes, alkynes, and aromatic compounds are organic compounds consisting solely of hydrogen and carbon atoms. They are therefore called **hydrocarbons**. Table 1 shows that the essential difference among these four types of hydrocarbons, besides the number of hydrogen and carbon atoms they contain, is the kind of carbon-to-carbon bond each contains. **Alkanes** have only single carbon-to-carbon bonds (C–C). Having single C–C bonds means that alkanes cannot further react with hydrogen, and are **saturated**. **Alkenes** contain at least one carbon-to-carbon double bond (C=C) and react with hydrogen under the right conditions. Thus, alkenes are said to be **unsaturated**. **Alkynes**, also unsaturated, contain a carbon-to-carbon triple bond (C≡C). **Aromatic compounds** contain carbon atoms in a ring structure and have unique unsaturated C=C double bonds. In aromatic compounds, each carbon atom in the ring shares electrons with all the carbons in the ring.

The C=C and C≡C bonds are important reaction sites that make it possible to differentiate unsaturated alkenes and alkynes from aromatic hydrocarbons and saturated alkanes, using simple reactions that react with the C=C or C≡C bond.

Two common qualitative tests for unsaturation in hydrocarbons and other organic compounds are the decoloration of an aqueous bromine (Br_2) solution and the decoloration of an aqueous potassium permanganate ($KMnO_4$) solution.

In the decoloration of bromine solution test, if the test compound is unsaturated, the orange-brown color of the aqueous bromine solution rapidly disappears, as shown in Equations 1 and 3. We call this an **addition reaction**, because bromine *adds* to each carbon of the bond. When this happens, the C=C and C≡C bonds become saturated.

A bromine solution does not react with every kind of unsaturated compound. It reacts with alkenes and alkynes, but not with the ring

Table 1 *Carbon bonding in alkanes, alkenes, alkynes, and aromatic compounds*

type of hydrocarbon	carbon bond type	saturation status	example
alkane	single (C–C)	saturated	ethane
alkene	double (C=C)	unsaturated	ethane
alkyne	triple (C≡C)	unsaturated	ethane
aromatic compound	shared electrons	unsaturated	benzene

structure of aromatic compounds. The shared electrons in the unsaturated bonds of the aromatic compound ring prevent aqueous bromine solution from reacting with them.

$$\text{ethene} + Br_2 \longrightarrow \text{colorless bromine addition product} \qquad \text{(Eq. 1)}$$

orange–brown

$$\text{benzene} + Br_2 \longrightarrow \text{no reaction} \qquad \text{(Eq. 2)}$$

$$\text{phenylethylene} + Br_2 \longrightarrow \text{colorless product} \qquad \text{(Eq. 3)}$$

Because solutions that are able to release bromine are hazardous, in the first test you will use an ethanolic solution of pyridinium bromide perbromide (PBP), instead of an aqueous bromine solution. PBP in ethanol is a less hazardous reagent than aqueous bromine solution. The structure of PBP is:

pyridinium bromide perbromide (PBP)

PBP liberates bromine in the presence of alkenes or alkynes. In solution, PBP is orange-brown. The solution becomes colorless as the bromine reacts with the alkene or alkyne, the same change as with aqueous Br_2. The color change indicates an addition product and a positive alkene or alkyne test.

In the permanganate test, an unsaturated compound reduces the purple permanganate ion (MnO_4^-), forming a precipitate of brown manganese(IV) oxide (manganese dioxide, MnO_2). Because $KMnO_4$ oxidizes the unsaturated compound, we call the reaction an **oxidation–reduction reaction**. As a result of this reaction, an OH group is added to each carbon at each end of a double bond in the alkene, as shown in Equation 4. When this happens, the C=C bond becomes saturated. The reaction looks like an addition reaction.

You will test only for alkenes in this experiment.

$$3\ H-\underset{\underset{H}{|}}{\overset{\overset{H}{|}}{C}}=\underset{\underset{H}{|}}{\overset{\overset{H}{|}}{C}}-H + 2\ MnO_4^- + 4\ H_2O \longrightarrow 3\ H-\underset{\underset{OH}{|}}{\overset{\overset{H}{|}}{C}}-\underset{\underset{OH}{|}}{\overset{\overset{H}{|}}{C}}-H + 2\ MnO_2 + 2\ OH^- \qquad (Eq.\ 4)$$

purple   brown solid

You will test seven known and two unknown organic compounds for C=C bond unsaturation. You will test each compound with PBP. A positive test for an alkene is indicated by a color change from an orange-brown solution to colorless solution. You will also test with aqueous potassium permanganate. A positive test for an alkene is indicated by a color change from a purple solution to a brown precipitate. Using these tests, you will distinguish alkenes from other compounds. Potassium permanganate, a strong oxidizing agent, can react with most organic compounds. However, at room temperature, the concentration of the potassium permanganate solution you will use, 2% aqueous potassium permanganate, will react rapidly only with alkenes.

PROCEDURE

Preview

- Prepare test tubes for PBP test
- Obtain samples to test
- Test samples with 2% PBP solution
- Observe and record PBP test results
- Prepare control and sample test tubes for the $KMnO_4$ test
- Test samples in acetone with 2% aqueous $KMnO_4$ solution
- Observe and record $KMnO_4$ test results
- Clean up

CHEMICAL ALERT

acetone—flammable and irritant
cyclohexane—highly flammable and irritant
cyclohexene—highly flammable and irritant
2% ethanolic pyridinium bromide perbromide—flammable, toxic, irritant, and lachrymator

2% aqueous potassium permanganate—oxidant and irritant
toluene—flammable and toxic
unknowns—flammable, toxic, corrosive, irritating, oxidizing, and/or carcinogenic

---

CAUTION

Wear departmentally approved eye protection while doing this experiment.

NOTE: The numbers appearing in parentheses indicate the specific lines on your Data Sheet on which the indicated data should be entered.

I. Reactions with 2% Ethanolic Pyridinium Bromide Perbromide (PBP)

CAUTION

The compounds used in this experiment can be flammable, toxic, corrosive, irritating, oxidizing, and/or carcinogenic. Use care when handling all reagents. If you spill any reagents, immediately notify your laboratory instructor.

CAUTION

Solid pyridinium bromide perbromide (PBP) is corrosive, a skin and respiratory irritant, and a mild lachrymator. A 2% ethanolic PBP solution is not a lachrymator, although it is flammable and toxic. When the alcohol evaporates from an ethanolic PBP solution spill, the result is solid PBP. Therefore, notify your laboratory instructor and clean up PBP solution spills promptly. Use soap and water to quickly wash off any PBP solution that gets on your skin. With the 2% ethanolic solution, avoid contact with combustible materials. Avoid ingesting either solid PBP or PBP solution.

---

1. Label nine 10×75-mm test tubes, one for each of the following substances: cyclohexane, cyclohexene, turpentine, 1-octene, toluene, mineral oil, canola oil, unknown 1, and unknown 2.

NOTE: If the test compound is a liquid, use 2 drops for the test. If the test compound is a solid, use about 20 mg for the test.

---

2. Obtain a sample of each of the nine compounds you will be testing in the appropriately labeled test tubes.

NOTE: When observing the PBP test, do not mistake dilution of orange-brown color by the test compound for a positive test. Also, if the reagent becomes colorless after you have added the first two drops but stops becoming colorless before you have added all 12 drops, it is likely that the test compound itself is saturated but contains a small amount of unsaturated compound as an impurity. Check with your laboratory instructor before recording this observation as a positive test.

---

3. Add two drops of 2% PBP to the cyclohexane test tube. Gently shake the tube to mix.

4. Observe the solution color. If there is no color change, go to Step 5. If there is a color change, record a brief description of it on your Data Sheet (1). Then slowly add 10 more drops of 2% PBP to the cyclohexane tube. If the solution remains colorless after you have added all 12 drops of PBP, record the results as a positive test for an alkene (2).

5. If the solution does not become colorless after you have added 2 drops of PBP, record the result as a negative test on your Data Sheet (2).

6. Test each of the remaining compounds by repeating Steps 3–5, substituting the appropriate test compound for cyclohexane.

cyclohexene	(3)	(4)	mineral oil	(11)	(12)
turpentine	(5)	(6)	canola oil	(13)	(14)
1-octene	(7)	(8)	unknown 1	(15)	(16)
toluene	(9)	(10)	unknown 2	(17)	(18)

II. Reactions with 2% Aqueous KMnO$_4$ Solution

CAUTION

2% Potassium permanganate solution is an oxidant and irritant that can cause skin discoloration. Prevent eye, skin, clothing, and combustible material contact. Avoid ingesting the solution. If you spill any solution, immediately notify your laboratory instructor.

Acetone is flammable and irritating. Do not use near open flames. Prevent eye, skin, and clothing contact. Avoid ingesting the compound. If you spill any acetone, immediately notify your laboratory instructor.

NOTE: When using this test, it may be necessary to allow the brown manganese(II) oxide to settle in order to determine whether or not the solution has changed color.

NOTE: You will need a control to compare with the liquids you test with the permanganate test. The control does not contain an alkene, so it should be purple, indicating a negative test. A brown precipitate indicates a positive test. Using the control, you can easily see whether each test is positive or negative.

7. Label a 10×75-mm test tube "control." Prepare the control solution by adding 1 mL of acetone and 3 drops of 2% KMnO$_4$ solution to the control test tube.

8. Label nine 10×75-mm test tubes, one for each of the solutions you are testing, and pour 1 mL of acetone into each. Add two drops of cyclohexane to the appropriately labeled tube.

NOTE: In Step 9, if the KMnO$_4$ changes color after you have added 2 drops but stops changing color before you have added all 20 drops, it is likely that the test compound itself is saturated but contains a small amount of an unsaturated compound as an impurity. The presence of such an impurity may cause the reaction solution to appear neither brown nor purple, but somewhere in between. If this occurs, check with your laboratory instructor before recording this result as a positive test.

9. Begin adding 2% aqueous $KMnO_4$ solution dropwise to the cyclohexane test tube. After adding each drop, gently tap the test tube to mix. Continue adding drops until either you reach 20 drops or the purple color persists after mixing.

   If the purple color still fades away after you have added 20 or more drops, record the solution color (19) and record the test as positive (20). If the purple color persists after you have added just 1 or 2 drops, record the solution color (19) and record the test as negative (20). In either case, compare the color of the reaction mixture to the control in order to verify the color change.

10. *Separately* test each of the remaining compounds by repeating Steps 8 and 9, substituting the appropriate test compound for cyclohexane. Record the results of your tests on your Data Sheet.

cyclohexene	(21)	(22)	mineral oil	(29)	(30)
turpentine	(23)	(24)	canola oil	(31)	(32)
1-octene	(25)	(26)	unknown 1	(33)	(34)
toluene	(27)	(28)	unknown 2	(35)	(36)

III. Cleaning Up

11. Place the reaction mixtures from Part I in the container provided by your laboratory instructor and labeled "Discarded PBP test solutions."

12. Place the reaction mixtures from Part II in the container provided by your laboratory instructor and labeled "Discarded $KMnO_4$ test solutions."

13. Place excess PBP reagent in the container labeled "Excess PBP reagent," provided by your laboratory instructor.

14. Place excess 2% aqueous $KMnO_4$ solution in the container provided by your laboratory instructor and labeled "Excess 2% aqueous $KMnO_4$ reagent."

15. Wash the test tubes and graduated cylinder with detergent, rinse with distilled water, and drain to dry.

CAUTION

Wash your hands thoroughly with soap or detergent before leaving the laboratory.

Name _____   _Section_ _____   _Date_ _____

Post-Laboratory Questions

(_Use the spaces provided for the answers and additional paper if necessary._)

1. Write equations that represent the following two reactions, including their products:

    (a) 1-octene + Br_2 →

    (b) 2-pentene + $KMnO_4$ →

2. The compounds shown below occur naturally in plants. Which of these compounds will test positive for unsaturation in alkenes or alkynes with 2% ethanolic PBP solution?

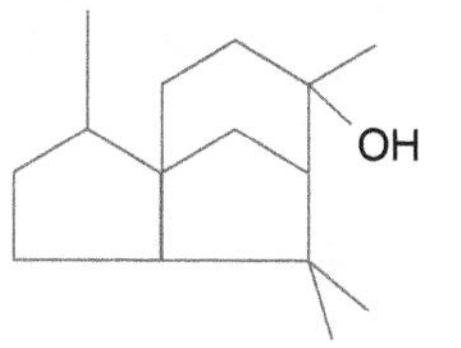

oil of cedar

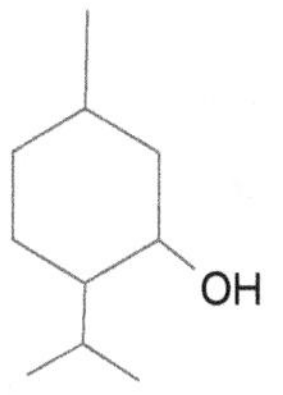

menthol, oil of peppermint

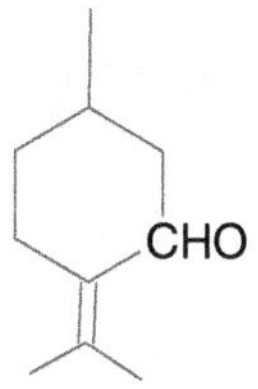

citronella

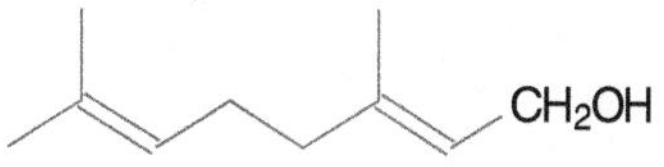

geraniol, oil of rose

3. Which of the cyclic compounds *A–E* will give a positive test for unsaturation in alkenes with 2% aqueous $KMnO_4$ solution?

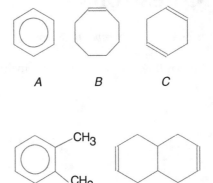

A   B   C

D   E

4. The use of saturated versus unsaturated cooking oils is a popular health topic. Suggest a way to modify the procedure in this experiment so that you could use it to determine the *relative* levels of unsaturation in various cooking oils.

_____   _____   _____
Name   *Section*   *Date*

Data Sheet

I. Reactions with 2% Ethanolic Pyridinium Bromide Perbromide (PBP)

test compound	number of drops of reagent added	observations	conclusion (+ or − test)
cyclohexane	_____	(1) _____	(2) _____
cyclohexene	_____	(3) _____	(4) _____
turpentine	_____	(5) _____	(6) _____
1-octene	_____	(7) _____	(8) _____
toluene	_____	(9) _____	(10) _____
mineral oil	_____	(11) _____	(12) _____
canola oil	_____	(13) _____	(14) _____
unknown 1	_____	(15) _____	(16) _____
unknown 2	_____	(17) _____	(18) _____

II. Reactions with 2% Aqueous KMnO₄ Solution

test compound	number of drops of reagent added	observations	conclusion (+ or − test)
cyclohexane	_____	(19) _____	(20) _____
cyclohexene	_____	(21) _____	(22) _____
turpentine	_____	(23) _____	(24) _____
1-octene	_____	(25) _____	(26) _____
toluene	_____	(27) _____	(28) _____
mineral oil	_____	(29) _____	(30) _____
canola oil	_____	(31) _____	(32) _____
unknown 1	_____	(33) _____	(34) _____
unknown 2	_____	(35) _____	(36) _____

Name   Section   Date

Pre-Laboratory Assignment

1. What precautions should be taken when handling a 2% ethanolic PBP solution?

2. Write an equation that represents the reaction of 2% ethanolic PBP solution with 4-methylcyclohexene,

H_3C —⬡

and name the product.

3. Write an equation that represents the reaction of 2% aqueous $KMnO_4$ solution with 3-hexene, $CH_3-CH_2-CH=CH-CH_2-CH_3$.

4. Write the structure of the product resulting from the reaction of

(a) With 2% ethanolic PBP solution.

(b) With 2% aqueous $KMnO_4$ solution.

Studying S_N1 and S_N2 Reactions: Nucleophilic Substitution at Saturated Carbon

Prepared by Jerry Manion, University of Central Arkansas

PURPOSE OF THE EXPERIMENT

Convert a primary alcohol to an alkyl bromide using an S_N2 reaction. Investigate some factors that influence the rate of S_N1 reactions.

EXPERIMENTAL OPTIONS

Synthesizing 1-Bromobutane Using Microscale Techniques
Synthesizing 1-Bromobutane Using Macroscale Techniques
Factors Affecting the Rates of S_N1 Reactions

BACKGROUND REQUIRED

You should be familiar with techniques used to dispense small amounts of liquid reagents and with techniques used to conduct microscale extractions. You should be familiar with reflux, distillation, and codistillation. You should know how to measure boiling points, refractive index, and density. You should be familiar with infrared spectroscopy. You should also be familiar with the nature of S_N1 and S_N2 reactions.

BACKGROUND INFORMATION

Substitution reactions, in which one atom or group of atoms replaces another, are commonly observed for organic compounds. Many substitution reactions involve a kind of reacting group called a nucleophile. A **nucleophile** contains an unshared pair of electrons that reacts with a site in an organic molecule that has a deficiency of electrons. Nucleophilic

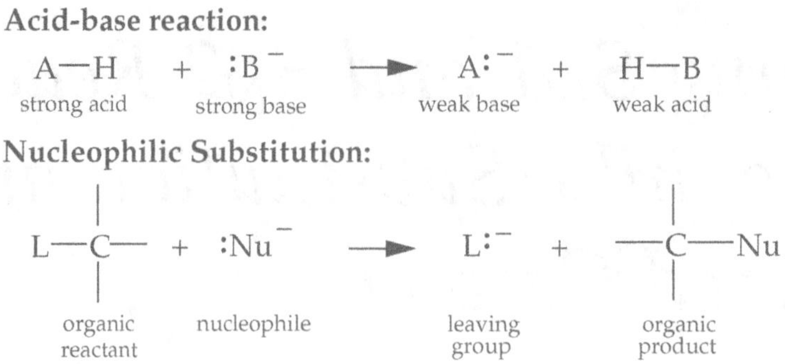

Acid-base reaction:

$$A\text{---}H \;\; + \;\; :B^- \;\;\longrightarrow\;\; A:^- \;\; + \;\; H\text{---}B$$

strong acid   strong base   weak base   weak acid

Nucleophilic Substitution:

$$L\text{---}\overset{|}{\underset{|}{C}}\text{---} \;\; + \;\; :Nu^- \;\;\longrightarrow\;\; L:^- \;\; + \;\; \text{---}\overset{|}{\underset{|}{C}}\text{---}Nu$$

organic   nucleophile   leaving   organic
reactant   group   product

Figure 1
Comparison of an acid–base reaction and a nucleophilic substitution reaction

substitution reactions share several characteristics with acid-base reactions, as shown in Figure 1.

Groups that are good leaving groups in nucleophilic substitution reactions are weak bases in acid–base reactions. Strong bases are typically good nucleophiles in substitution reactions. In an acid–base reaction, a proton is transferred from the conjugate acid of a weak base to a strong base. In a similar fashion, nucleophilic substitution reactions often involve the transfer of a carbon group from a weak base, the leaving group, to a stronger base, the nucleophile.

Nucleophilic substitution reactions may occur by one of two common mechanisms, designated S_N2 and S_N1.

S_N2 Mechanism

The S_N2 mechanism derives its designation from the fact that *two* chemical species—the organic reactant and the nucleophile—participate in the rate-determining step of the reaction. This mechanism has only one step, as shown in Equation 1.

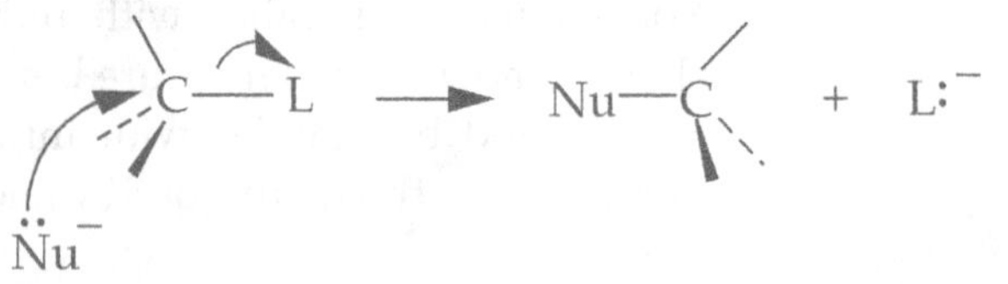

$$\overset{\diagdown}{\underset{\diagup}{C}}\text{---}L \;\longrightarrow\; Nu\text{---}\overset{\diagup}{\underset{\diagdown}{C}} \;+\; L:^- \qquad\qquad \text{(Eq. 1)}$$

$$Nu^-$$

The reaction is initiated by an attack of the nucleophile on the carbon bonded to the leaving group. This *back-side* attack produces a product in which the configuration of the carbon atom is inverted.

Some factors that can have a significant effect on the rate of S_N2 reactions include:

(1) The leaving group: Leaving groups are invariably weak bases. The presence of a good leaving group in the organic compound is essential for a nucleophilic substitution reaction to occur.

(2) The carbon group: An S_N2 reaction occurs fastest when the approach of the nucleophile to the carbon is unhindered by the presence of bulky groups. For example, the reaction occurs faster at primary carbon atoms than at secondary carbon atoms.

(3) The nucleophile: For nucleophiles in which the attacking atoms are of comparable size, nucleophilicity parallels basicity. That is, stronger bases are better nucleophiles than weaker bases. When nucleophiles differ in size, however, the larger, more polarizable atoms are more nucleophilic, even though they are weaker bases.

(4) The solvent: Reactions involving negatively charged nucleophiles occur much more rapidly in *polar-aprotic* solvents; that is, solvents in which anionic nucleophiles are poorly solvated. Dimethylsulfoxide (DMSO) is an example of a polar-aprotic solvent.

S$_N$1 Mechanism

Nucleophilic substitution reactions may occur via an S$_N$1 mechanism, in which *only* the organic reactant is involved in the rate-determining step, as shown in Equation 2. The nucleophile reacts in a fast step.

$$-\overset{|}{\underset{|}{C}}-L \xrightarrow{\text{slow}} -\overset{+}{C}\Big\langle \xrightarrow[\text{fast}]{:Nu-H} -\overset{|}{\underset{|}{C}}-\overset{+}{\underset{H}{Nu}} \xrightarrow[\text{fast}]{-H^+} -\overset{|}{\underset{|}{C}}-Nu \qquad \text{(Eq. 2)}$$

S$_N$1 reactions occur when conditions favor ionization of the organic reactant. Such conditions include:

(1) The leaving group: The leaving group (L) must be a weak base.

(2) The carbon group: The rate-determining step involves production of a carbocation. This step will occur faster for those compounds that yield more stable carbocations. For example, tertiary compounds react faster than secondary compounds. Primary compounds react extremely slowly. Carbocation intermediates are also stabilized by dispersal of the positive charge through delocalization of electrons. S$_N$1 reactions that produce such resonance-stabilized carbocation intermediates are also quite fast. For example, S$_N$1 reactions occur readily with molecules that form allyl or benzyl carbocations.

(3) The solvent: Ionization processes are facilitated by polar solvents. Because the rate of an S$_N$1 reaction is directly dependent on such an ionization, the reaction occurs faster in more polar solvents.

In the first part of this experiment, you will convert 1-butanol to 1-bromobutane as an example of an S$_N$2 reaction. Because the OH group of the alcohol is not a weak base and, therefore, not a good leaving group, you will conduct the reaction in a strongly acidic solution. In an acidic environment, the alcohol exists as its conjugate acid, and the leaving group is a water molecule, a weak base, as shown in Equation 3.

$$CH_3CH_2CH_2CH_2{-}OH \xrightarrow{H^+} CH_3CH_2CH_2CH_2{-}\overset{+}{O}H_2 \xrightarrow[S_N2]{Br^-} CH_3CH_2CH_2CH_2{-}Br + H_2O \qquad \text{(Eq. 3)}$$

1-butanol   1-bromobutane

The relatively uncrowded primary carbon atom is open to back-side attack by an appropriate nucleophile. Most nucleophiles are strong bases and could not exist in this acidic environment because they would be rapidly protonated. Bromide ion, however, is a vey weak base that is strongly nucleophilic due to its very large size. Bromide ion is an effective nucleophile even in a very acidic medium.

In the second part of this experiment, you will study factors affecting the rates of S$_N$1 reactions. In S$_N$1 reactions, solvent molecules often serve as the nucleophile. Such reactions are called **solvolysis** reactions. The reaction of 2-bromo-2-methylpropane with water is shown in Equation 4.

$$CH_3-\underset{\underset{CH_3}{|}}{\overset{\overset{CH_3}{|}}{C}}-Br \quad + \quad H_2O \quad \longrightarrow \quad CH_3-\underset{\underset{CH_3}{|}}{\overset{\overset{CH_3}{|}}{C}}-OH \quad + \quad HBr \qquad (Eq.\ 4)$$

2-bromo-2-methylpropane   2-methyl-2-propanol

The HBr formed as a byproduct is a strong acid and is completely ionized in the solution. As the reaction occurs, the acidity of the solution increases, providing a convenient means for monitoring the rate of the reaction. In this experiment, monitoring is initiated by placing a measured quantity of base into the solution. As the S_N1 reaction proceeds, the generated acid neutralizes the base. An acid–base indicator added to the reaction solution changes color at the point when all of the base has been neutralized. The shorter the time period required for this neutralization, the faster the S_N1 reaction has proceeded.

You will investigate three factors that affect the rate of S_N1 reactions: the identity of the leaving group, Br^- versus Cl^-; the structure of the alkyl group, $3°$ versus $2°$; and the polarity of the solvent, 40 percent 2-propanol versus 60 percent 2-propanol.

SYNTHESIZING 1-BROMOBUTANE

Using Microscale Techniques

Equipment

2 beakers, 100-mL
2 boiling chips, acid-resistant
15-mL centrifuge tube
125-mL Erlenmeyer flask
glass stirring rod
25-mL graduated cylinder
6 Pasteur pipets, with latex bulb
1.0-mL pipet

2.0-mL pipet
sand bath*
support stand
13 × 100-mm test tube[†]
18 × 150-mm test tube
2 vials, 5-mL[†]
utility clamp

*sand in crystallizing dish on electric hot plate or sand in electric heating well with heat controller
[†]extra equipment for optional procedure, **3. Distilling the Product**

Reagents and Properties

substance	quantity	molar mass (g/mol)	bp (°C)	density (g/mL)	n_D^{20}
1-bromobutane*		137.0	102	1.276	1.4390
1-butanol	1.00 g	74.1	118	0.810	1.3990
calcium chloride, anhydrous	0.4 g				

substance	quantity	molar mass (g/mol)	bp (°C)	density (g/mL)	n_D^{20}
hydrobromic acid, 48%	2.0 mL	80.9		1.49	
sulfuric acid, concentrated	1.0 mL	98.1		1.84	
sodium hydrogen carbonate, 5% aqueous	2 mL			1.04	

* product

Preview

- Place a boiling chip, 1-butanol, and HBr solution into a test tube
- Slowly add concentrated H_2SO_4
- Heat at reflux for 1 hr
- Allow the reaction mixture to cool, then separate the acid layer
- Wash the organic layer with water, aqueous $NaHCO_3$, then water again
- Dry the organic layer with anhydrous $CaCl_2$
- Purify the product by distillation
- Characterize the product by boiling point, refractive index, density, or IR spectroscopy

PROCEDURE

CHEMICAL ALERT

1-bromobutane—*flammable and irritant*
1-butanol—*flammable and irritant*
48% hydrobromic acid—*toxic and corrosive*
sulfuric acid—*toxic and oxidizer*

CAUTION

Wear departmentally approved safety goggles at all times while in the chemistry laboratory.

1. Conducting the Reaction

CAUTION

Hydrobromic acid (HBr) is toxic and corrosive. Concentrated sulfuric acid (H_2SO_4) is toxic and oxidizing. HBr and H_2SO_4 can cause severe burns. In case of spill, notify your laboratory instructor immediately.

1-Butanol is flammable and irritating. Do not use near flames or other heat sources. Prevent eye, skin, and clothing contact. Avoid inhaling fumes and ingesting these compounds.

NOTE 1: As the reaction occurs, you should note the production of a second liquid layer. One layer contains the water and acid; the other contains 1-bromo-butane produced by the reaction.

NOTE 2: Once the liquid in the test tube reaches a steady reflux condition, proceed with the section "Factors Affecting the Rates of S_N1 Reactions" later in this module.

Insert an 18 × 150-mm test tube into a 125-mL Erlenmeyer flask. Place the flask on a balance and tare the balance. Add 1.00 g of 1-butanol to the test tube. Add 2.0 mL of 48% HBr and an *acid resistant* boiling chip. Then *slowly* add, with mixing, 1.0 mL of concentrated H_2SO_4.

Remove the test tube from the Erlenmeyer flask. Clamp the test tube vertically to a support stand with *only the very bottom* of the tube in a sand bath. Heat the mixture to boiling using a low setting.

Avoid loss of HBr; do not allow the condensation ring to rise more than 2 cm in the test tube. Reflux the solution for 1 hr. [NOTE 1] [NOTE 2]

2. Washing the Reaction Mixture

CAUTION

1-Bromobutane is flammable and irritating. Do not use near flames or other heat sources. Prevent eye, skin, and clothing contact. Avoid inhaling fumes and ingesting 1-bromobutane.

Label two 100-mL beakers "Acid Layer" and "Washes", respectively. Place 25 mL of distilled or deionized water into the beaker labeled "Acid Layer".

After the reflux is complete, remove the test tube from the sand bath. Allow the test tube to cool.

Transfer the contents of the test tube to a 15-mL centrifuge tube. Use a Pasteur pipet to remove the bottom acid layer. Place the acid layer into the beaker labeled "Acid Layer".

To wash the 1-bromobutane layer, add 2 mL of water to the centrifuge tube and mix well. Then use a Pasteur pipet to remove the upper water layer. Place the water into the beaker labeled "Washes".

Wash the 1-bromobutane again, first with 2 mL of 5% aqueous sodium hydrogen carbonate ($NaHCO_3$), then with a second 2 mL of water. Each time, use the Pasteur pipet to remove the aqueous layer and place the layer into the beaker labeled "Washes".

After the final washing with water, allow the two layers to *completely* separate. Use a clean Pasteur pipet to transfer the 1-bromobutane layer to a clean, dry 5-mL vial.

NOTE 3: As the solid anhydrous $CaCl_2$ removes water from the liquid 1-bromo-butane, the liquid layer will become clear. Swirling the mixture will facilitate the process.

Add 4–5 granules of anhydrous $CaCl_2$ to the vial to dry the product. Allow the product to dry for 5–10 min. [NOTE 3]

If you do not conduct the optional distillation in Part 3, measure and record the mass of your product.

3. Distilling the Product (optional)

Tare a 5-mL vial. Use a clean, dry Pasteur pipet to transfer the product to a clean, dry 13 × 100-mm test tube. Add a boiling chip. Clamp the test tube vertically in a sand bath and heat the product until the liquid refluxes in the test tube.

Submerge the tip of a clean, dry Pasteur pipet into the 1-bromobutane vapors, as shown in Figure 2. Draw the vapors into the pipet, where they will condense. Transfer the condensed 1-bromobutane to the tared 5-mL vial.

Repeat this process until no more vapors are obtained. Measure and record the mass of the 1-bromobutane collected.

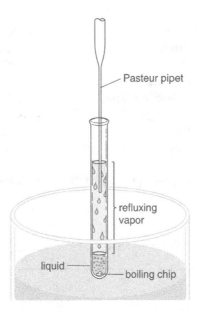

Figure 2
Test-tube distillation apparatus

4. Characterizing the Product [NOTE 4]

NOTE 4: Use the product characterization techniques designated by your laboratory instructor.

Characterize the product by measuring its boiling point, density, or refractive index. Record the temperature when measuring the refractive index. Make a temperature correction for the refractive index. [NOTE 5] Compare your experimental values with the literature values given under Reagents and Properties.

Obtain an infrared spectrum of your product. Compare your product spectrum with a spectrum of the 1-butanol used as the reagent. Pay particular attention to the regions at 3500 cm^{-1} and 1050 cm^{-1}.

5. Cleaning Up

NOTE 5: The refractive index at 20°C is calculated by using the following equation, where T is the ambient temperature in degrees Celsius, and n^T_D is the refractive index measured at ambient temperature.

$$n^{20}_D = n^T_D + 0.00045 \ (T - 20\,^{\circ}C)$$

Place your recovered materials in the appropriate labeled collection containers as directed by your laboratory instructor. Clean your glassware with soap or detergent.

CAUTION

Wash your hands thoroughly with soap or detergent before leaving the laboratory.

SYNTHESIZING 1-BROMOBUTANE

Using Macroscale Techniques

Equipment

50-mL beaker	10-mL graduated cylinder
400-mL beaker*	2 Pasteur pipets,
boiling chip, acid-resistant	with latex bulb†
15-mL centrifuge tube	product vial†
100-mL flask heater,	rubber stopper, one-hole
with heat controller	rubber tubing

standard taper glassware:
  condenser, with tubing
  distilling head
  10-mL round-bottom flask[†]
  100-mL round-bottom flask
  thermometer, −10–260 °C,
    with adapter
  vacuum adapter

support ring
2 support stands
18 × 150-mm test tube
2 utility clamps
Y-tube or T-tube[‡]

*for ice bath
[†]extra equipment for optional procedure, **4. Distilling the Product**
[‡]for gas trap

Reagents and Properties

substance	quantity	molar mass (g/mol)	bp (°C)	density (g/mL)	n_D^{20}
1-bromobutane*		137.0	102	1.276	1.4390
1-butanol	5.0 g	74.1	118	0.810	1.3990
calcium chloride, anhydrous	1.0 g				
hydrobromic acid, 48%	10.0 mL	80.9		1.49	
sulfuric acid, concentrated	4.0 mL	98.1		1.841	
sodium hydrogen carbonate, 5% aqueous	5.0 mL			1.04	

*product

Preview

- Place a boiling chip, 1-butanol, and HBr solution into a roundbottom flask
- Slowly add concentrated H_2SO_4 to the cooled reaction mixture
- Heat the mixture at reflux for 1 hr
- Codistill the product with water
- Wash the organic layer with water, 5% $NaHCO_3$, then water again
- Dry the organic layer with anhydrous $CaCl_2$
- Purify the product by distillation
- Characterize the product by boiling point, refractive index, density, or IR spectroscopy

PROCEDURE

CHEMICAL ALERT

1-bromobutane—*flammable and irritant*
1-butanol—*flammable and irritant*

48% hydrobromic acid—*toxic and corrosive*

sulfuric acid—*toxic and oxidizer*

> **CAUTION**
>
> Wear departmentally approved safety goggles at all times while in the chemistry laboratory.

1. Conducting the Reaction

> **CAUTION**
>
> Hydrobromic acid (HBr) is toxic and corrosive. Concentrated sulfuric acid (H_2SO_4) is toxic and oxidizing. HBr and H_2SO_4 can cause severe burns. In case of a spill, notify your laboratory instructor immediately.
>
> 1-Butanol is flammable and irritating. Do not use near flames or other heat sources. Prevent eye, skin, and clothing contact. Avoid inhaling fumes and ingesting these compounds.

Use the 400-mL beaker to prepare an ice-water bath. Place an *acid resistant* boiling chip, 5.0 g (6.2 mL) of 1-butanol, and 10 mL of 48% HBr into a 100-mL round-bottom flask. Cool the mixture in the ice bath. *Slowly* add to the round-bottom flask, with stirring, 4 mL of concentrated H_2SO_4.

Fit the flask with a condenser for reflux, as shown in Figure 3. Fit the top of the condenser with a rubber stopper equipped with a Y-tube. Use rubber tubing to connect one arm of the Y-tube to the water aspirator. Leave the other arm open. Turn on the water to the aspirator to draw the acid fumes generated by the reaction.

Heat the mixture to boiling. Reflux the mixture gently for 1 hr. [NOTE 6] [NOTE 7]

NOTE 6: As the reaction occurs, you should note the production of a second liquid layer. One layer contains the water and acid; the other contains 1-bromobutane produced by the reaction.

NOTE 7: Once the liquid in the flask reaches a steady reflux condition, proceed with the section "Factors Affecting the Rates of S_N1 Reactions" on the page 11.

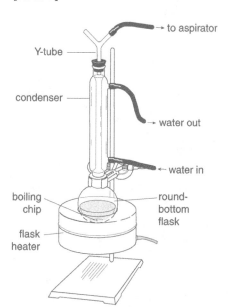

Figure 3
Reflux apparatus for macro-scale preparation

© 1998 Cengage Learning

2. Codistillation of the Product

1-Bromobutane is flammable and irritating. Do not use near flames or other heat sources. Prevent eye, skin, and clothing contact. Avoid inhaling fumes and ingesting 1-bromobutane.

Once the reflux is complete, remove the heater from the flask and allow the flask to cool. Add 10 mL of distilled or deionized water and an additional boiling chip.

Arrange the apparatus for distillation, as shown in Figure 4. Distill the mixture into an 18×150-mm test tube until you collect 10–15 mL of distillate. [NOTE 8]

Place the pot residue in the container labeled "Recovered Pot Residue", provided by your laboratory instructor.

NOTE 8: You will observe two layers in the test tube because the 1-bromobutane will codistill with water. Once you collect 10–15 mL of distillate, only water should remain in the pot.

3. Washing the Product

Label a 50-mL beaker "Washes". Use a Pasteur pipet to remove the upper aqueous layer from the distillate. Place this layer into the labeled beaker.

To wash the 1-bromobutane layer, add 5 mL of water to the test tube and mix well. Use a Pasteur pipet to remove the water layer and transfer the water to the labeled beaker.

Wash the 1-bromobutane again, first with 5 mL of 5% aqueous sodium hydrogen carbonate ($NaHCO_3$), then with a second 5 mL of water. Each

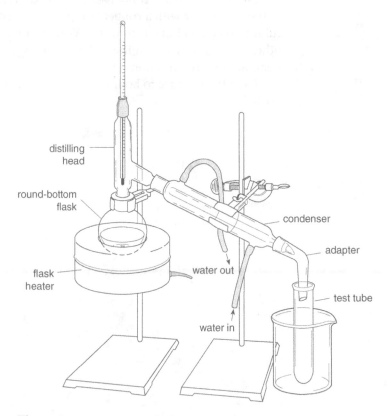

Figure 4
Apparatus for codistillation

time, use the Pasteur pipet to remove the aqueous layer and place the layer into the labeled beaker.

After the last water wash, remove as much of the water as possible with the Pasteur pipet. Transfer the contents of the test tube to a centrifuge tube to facilitate the removal of the water. Again, remove as much water as possible.

Add approximately 1 g of anhydrous $CaCl_2$ to dry the product. Allow the product to dry for 5–10 min. [NOTE 9]

If you do not conduct the optional distillation in Part 4, measure and record the mass of your product.

NOTE 9: The liquid layer becomes clear as the solid anhydrous $CaCl_2$ extracts water from the liquid 1-bromobutane.

4. Distilling the Product (Optional)

Tare a product vial. Use a clean, dry Pasteur pipet to transfer the dried 1-bromobutane into a 10-mL round-bottom flask. Assemble a distillation apparatus using the 10-mL round-bottom flask. Make certain the distillation apparatus is clean and dry.

Distill the product into the tared vial, collecting the portion that distills from 99–103 °C. Measure and record the mass of the 1-bromobutane collected.

5. Characterizing the Product [NOTE 10]

NOTE 10: Use the product characterization techniques designated by your laboratory instructor.

Characterize the product by measuring its boiling point, density, or refractive index. Record the temperature when measuring the refractive index. Make a temperature correction for the refractive index. [NOTE 11] Compare the experimental values with the literature values given under Reagents and Properties.

Obtain an infrared spectrum of your product. Compare your product spectrum with a spectrum of the 1-butanol used as the reagent. Pay particular attention to the regions at 3500 cm^{-1} and 1050 cm^{-1}.

6. Cleaning Up

NOTE 11: The refractive index at 20 °C is calculated by using the following equation, where T is the ambient temperature in degrees Celsius, and n_D^T is the refractive index measured at ambient temperature.

$$n_D^{20} = n_D^T + 0.00045(T - 20\,°C)$$

Place your recovered materials in the appropriate labeled collection containers as directed by your laboratory instructor. Clean your glassware with soap or detergent.

CAUTION

Wash your hands thoroughly with soap or detergent before leaving the laboratory.

FACTORS AFFECTING THE RATES OF S$_N$1 REACTIONS

Equipment

2 Erlenmeyer flasks, 125-mL
50-mL graduated cylinder
100-mL graduated cylinder
marking pen
*or adjustable micropipet set to 200-μL

50-μL micropipet
100-μL micropipet*
timer

Reagents and Properties

substance	quantity	molar mass (g/mol)	bp (°C)	density (g/mL)	n_D^{20}
2-bromopropane	50 µL	123.0	59	1.31	1.4250
2-propanol	150 mL	60.1	82	0.79	1.3770
0.5M sodium hydroxide	1.2 mL				
phenolphthalein	30 drops				
2-bromo-2-methyl propane	200 µL	137	73	1.19	1.4279
2-chloro-2-methyl propane	50 µL	92.6	52	0.85	1.3848

Preview

Measuring the Effect of the Leaving Group on Reaction Rate

- Prepare a 50% 2-propanol/water solvent mixture
- Divide the mixture into two portions
- Add phenolphthalein indicator and NaOH solution
- Add alkyl halides and measure the time required for discharge of the indicator color

Measuring the Effect of the Alkyl Group Structure on Reaction Rate

- Prepare a 50% 2-propanol/water solvent mixture
- Divide the mixture into two portions
- Add phenolphthalein indicator and NaOH solution
- Add alkyl halides and measure the time required for discharge of the indicator color

Measuring the Effect of Solvent Polarity on Reaction Rate

- Prepare 40% and 60% 2-propanol/water solvent mixtures
- Add phenolphthalein indicator and NaOH solution
- Add 2-bromo-2-methylpropane and measure the time required for discharge of the indicator color

PROCEDURE

CHEMICAL ALERT

2-bromopropane—*flammable and irritant*

2-bromo-2-methylpropane—*flammable*

2-chloro-2-methylpropane—*flammable*

2-propanol—*flammable and irritant*

sodium hydroxide—*corrosive and toxic*

CAUTION

Wear departmentally approved safety goggles at all times while in the chemistry laboratory.

1. Measuring the Effect of the Leaving Group on Reaction Rate

CAUTION

2-Bromo-2-methylpropane, 2-chloro-2-methylpropane, and 2-propanol are flammable and irritating. Do not use near flames or other heat sources. Prevent eye, skin, and clothing contact. Avoid breathing fumes and ingesting these compounds.

To prepare a 50% mixture of 2-propanol in water, place 50 mL of 2-propanol into a 100-mL graduated cylinder and add enough distilled or deionized water to make 100 mL. Mix well. Place 50 mL of the mixture into each of two 125-mL Erlenmeyer flasks.

Add 5 drops of phenolphthalein indicator and *exactly* 200 µL of 0.5*M* NaOH to each of the flasks. Mix well. [NOTE 12]

NOTE 12: The phenolphthalein should be bright pink in this slightly basic solution.

Add 50 µL of 2-bromo-2-methylpropane, with swirling, to one of the flasks. Measure and record the time required for the solution to become colorless.

Add 50 µL of 2-chloro-2-methylpropane, with swirling, to the second flask. Again measure and record the time required for the solution to become colorless.

2. Measuring the Effect of the Alkyl Group Structure on Reaction Rate

CAUTION

2-Bromopropane, 2-bromo-2-methylpropane, and 2-propanol are flammable and irritating. Do not use near flames or other heat sources. Prevent eye, skin, and clothing contact. Avoid breathing fumes and ingesting these compounds.

Prepare 100 mL of a 50% mixture of 2-propanol in water as described in Part 1. Divide the mixture equally between two 125-mL Erlenmeyer flasks.

Add 5 drops of phenolphthalein and *exactly* 200 µL of 0.5*M* NaOH to each of the flasks. Mix well.

Add 50 µL of 2-bromo-2-methylpropane, with swirling, to one of the flasks. Measure and record the time required for the solution to become colorless.

Add 50 µL of 2-bromopropane, with swirling, to the second flask. Again measure and record the time required for the solution to become colorless. If the solution does not become colorless within 15 min, stop the reaction and record the time as >15 min.

3. Measuring the Effect of Solvent Polarity on Reaction Rate

CAUTION

2-Bromo-2-methylpropane and 2-propanol are flammable and irritating. Do not use near flames or other heat sources. Prevent eye, skin, and clothing contact. Avoid breathing fumes and ingesting these compounds.

To prepare 50 mL of a 40% mixture of 2-propanol in water, place 20 mL of 2-propanol into a 50-mL graduated cylinder and add enough water to make 50 mL. Place the mixture into a labeled 125-mL Erlenmeyer flask.

To prepare 50 mL of a 60% mixture of 2-propanol in water, place 30 mL of 2-propanol into a 50-mL graduated cylinder and add enough water to make 50 mL. Place the mixture into a labeled 125-mL Erlenmeyer flask.

Add 5 drops of phenolphthalein and *exactly* 200 μL of 0.5*M* NaOH to each flask. Mix well.

Add 50 μL of 2-bromo-2-methylpropane, with swirling, to each flask. Measure and record the time required for each solution to become colorless.

4. Cleaning Up

NOTE 13: If you conducted this section of the experiment during the reflux time for Section I or II, return to that section.

Place all alcohol-water reaction mixtures in the container labeled "Recovered Alcohol-Water Mixtures", provided by your laboratory instructor. Clean your glassware with soap or detergent. [NOTE 13]

CAUTION

Wash your hands thoroughly with soap or detergent before leaving the laboratory.

Name _____   Section _____   Date _____

Post-Laboratory Questions

1. Calculate the percent yield of 1-bromobutane obtained in your experiment.

2. What experimental evidence can you provide that the product isolated in your synthetic experiment is 1-bromobutane?

3. Which compound, 2-bromo-2-methylpropane or 2-chloro-2-methyl-propane, reacted faster in your S_N1 experiment? What were the relative rates of the two reactions?

4. Based on your answer to question 3, which is the better leaving group, Br^- or Cl^-? Are these results consistent with the relative basicities of these two ions? Briefly explain.

5. Which compound, 2-bromo-2-methylpropane or 2-bromopropane, reacted faster in your S_N1 experiment? How are the reactivities of 2-bromo-2-methylpropane and 2-bromopropane related to the stabilities of the carbocations produced as intermediates in the reaction? Briefly explain.

6. Which of the two solvent mixtures, 40% 2-propanol or 60% 2-propanol, is more polar? Briefly explain.

7. In which of the two solvent mixtures did 2-bromo-2-methylpropane react faster? Account for your results in terms of the effect of solvent polarity on the rate-determining step in this S_N1 reaction.

8. Use your results to explain which variable—leaving group, alkyl structure, or solvent polarity—has the greatest impact on the rate of an S_N1 reaction.

_____   _____   _____

Pre-Laboratory Assignment

1. Why should care be exercised in handling concentrated acids such as H_2SO_4 and HBr?

2. Why do primary alkyl halides typically undergo S_N2 substitution reactions more rapidly than do secondary or tertiary alkyl halides?

3. Why should reflux of the microscale reaction mixture be gentle, with the condensation ring remaining close to the surface of the liquid in the test tube?

4. By observing the reaction mixture, what visual evidence can be gained to indicate that 1-butanol is being converted to 1-bromobutane?

5. What is the function of anhydrous $CaCl_2$ in this experiment?

6. The limiting reagent in the production of 1-bromobutane is 1-butanol. Calculate the theoretical yield of 1-bromobutane for your experiment. Record your results here and in your laboratory notebook.

7. How does the S_N1 reaction in this experiment cause the acid-base indicator, phenolphthalein, to change color? Briefly explain.

8. Why is it important that the volume of $0.5M$ NaOH be measured exactly?

9. Which is the stronger acid, HCl or HBr? Which is the stronger base, Cl^- or Br^-?

Dehydrating Cyclohexanol

Prepared by Carl T. Wigal, Lebanon Valley College

PURPOSE OF THE EXPERIMENT

Dehydrate cyclohexanol to prepare cyclohexene. Characterize cyclohexene by using ammonium cerium (IV) nitrate test, bromine test, infrared spectroscopy and/or refractive index.

EXPERIMENTAL OPTIONS

Semi-Microscale Dehydration
Microscale Dehydration
    Using Glassware with Elastomeric Connectors
    Using a Hickman Still Assembly
Product Characterization

BACKGROUND REQUIRED

You should be familiar with basic laboratory techniques for measuring volumes and masses. You should know how to conduct a simple distillation. For product characterization, you should know how to measure refractive index and/or obtain and interpret an infrared spectrum.

BACKGROUND INFORMATION

Elimination reactions involve the loss of a small molecule (H–X) from adjacent carbon atoms, resulting in pi-bond formation. Consequently, elimination reactions are good synthetic methods for producing alkenes or alkynes. These reactions occur through a process called heterolytic bond cleavage. **Heterolytic bond cleavage** occurs when one atom leaves a compound with both electrons of the original bond, resulting in the formation of ions. For example, elimination of H–X from an organic molecule involves the loss of a proton (H^+) and a leaving group (X^-), as shown in Figure 1 on the next page. The leaving group departs with both electrons from the original C–X bond. The electrons in the adjacent C–H bond form the new pi bond of the alkene, with loss of the proton.

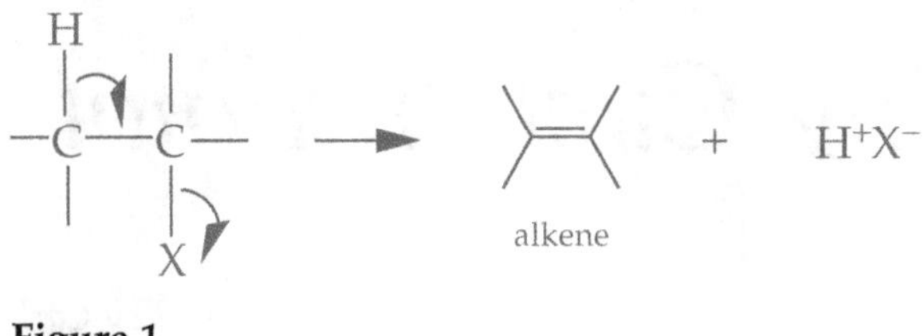

Figure 1
Elimination of HX from an organic molecule

The elimination of water (H–OH) from alcohols was one of the earliest organic reactions studied. This reaction, still widely used, is called a **dehydration reaction**. In many cases, alcohol dehydration is an acid-catalyzed reaction that proceeds by an elimination mechanism called **E1**. The E1 mechanism for the dehydration of 2-methyl-2-butanol is shown in Figure 2.

The first step of dehydration is a proton transfer from the acid catalyst to the oxygen atom of the alcohol. This protonation forms an **oxonium ion**, the conjugate acid of the alcohol. Weak bases are good leaving groups, so changing the leaving group from hydroxide to water favors the reaction.

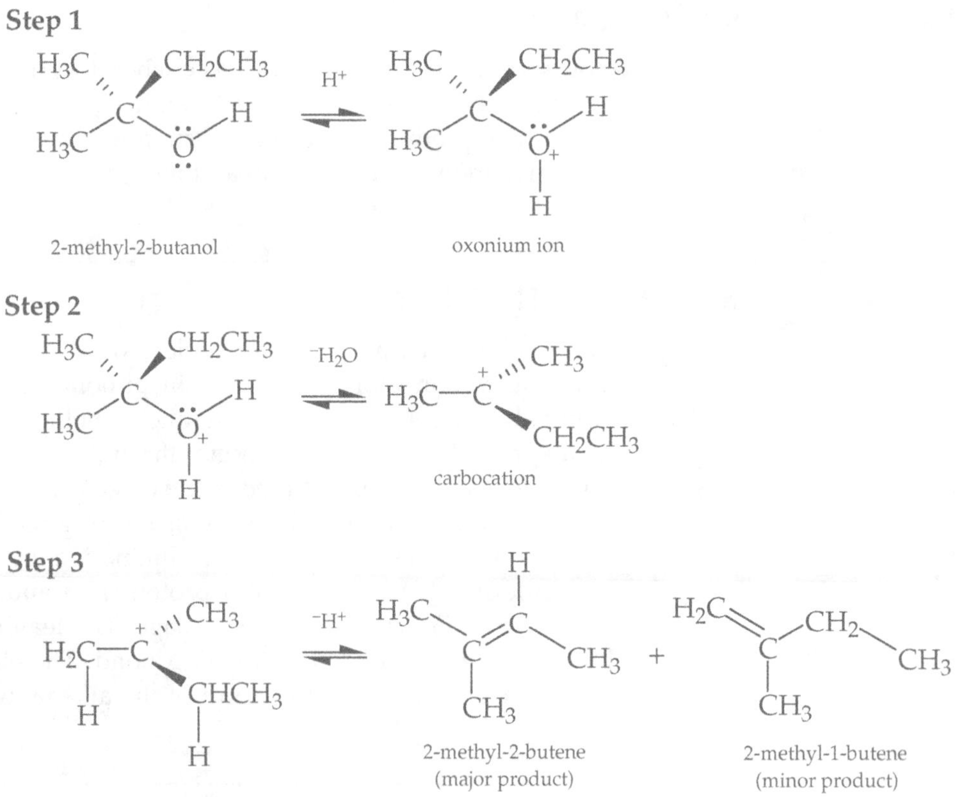

Step 1

2-methyl-2-butanol   oxonium ion

Step 2

carbocation

Step 3

2-methyl-2-butene (major product)   2-methyl-1-butene (minor product)

Figure 2
E1 mechanism for the dehydration of 2-methyl-2-butanol

The second step of the dehydration reaction is loss of water from the oxonium ion forming a positively charged **carbocation**. This step of the mechanism is rate-determining.

Not all alcohols dehydrate at the same rate. Alcohols are classified according to the number of alkyl groups attached to the carbon bearing the hydroxyl group. The terminology used to describe the degree of substitution is **tertiary (3°)**, **secondary (2°)**, and **primary (1°)**. Experimental evidence shows that the ease of alcohol dehydration follows the trend 3° > 2° > 1°. This reactivity directly relates to the stability of the carbocation intermediate formed during the rate-determining step of the reaction.

In the third and final step, a proton is released from a carbon atom adjacent to the positively charged carbon. The electrons previously comprising the C–H bond form the new carbon–carbon pi bond.

The formation of two isomeric alkenes is possible in elimination reactions where a proton can be lost from either of two different carbon atoms. **Saytzeff's rule** states that the orientation of the double bond favors the more thermodynamically stable alkene; that is, the alkene with the greatest number of alkyl groups bonded to the carbons of the double bond. Thus, dehydrating 2-methyl-2-butanol produces primarily 2-methyl-2-butene, a trisubstituted alkene, rather than 2-methyl-1-butene, a disubstituted alkene.

In this experiment, you will dehydrate cyclohexanol to form cyclohexene. Because cyclohexene has a lower boiling point than cyclohexanol, the cyclohexene can be distilled away as it forms. You will isolate and characterize the cyclohexene by performing qualitative tests for alcohols and alkenes. Your laboratory instructor will tell you whether to further characterize the cyclohexene by measuring its refractive index and/or by generating infrared spectra for both cyclohexanol and cyclohexene.

Qualitative Tests

The presence of the hydroxyl group of an alcohol can be determined by observing the reaction of an alcohol with ammonium cerium(IV) nitrate, $(NH_4)_2Ce(NO_3)_6$. A positive test for an alcohol is indicated as the yellow $(NH_4)_2Ce(NO_3)_6$ solution turns red when complexed with an alcohol, as shown in Figure 3. Even small contaminating amounts of alcohol can cause a slight color change.

The presence of a carbon–carbon double bond of an alkene can be determined by observing the reaction between bromine and an alkene, as shown in Figure 4 on the next page. Bromine is a reddish-brown color. A positive test is indicated by the decolorization of the bromine solution.

$$(NH_4)_2Ce(NO_3)_6 \ + \ R{-}OH \ \longrightarrow \ [\text{alcohol + reagent}]$$

yellow　　　　　　　alcohol　　　　　　　red complex

Figure 3
Reaction of ammonium cerium(IV) nitrate with an alcohol

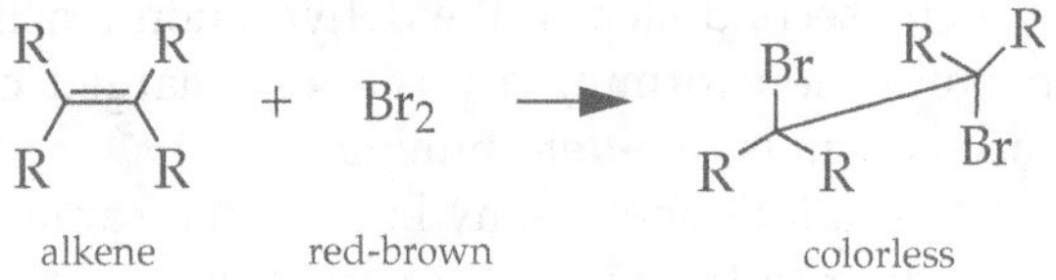

Figure 4
Reaction of bromine with an alkene

SEMI-MICROSCALE DEHYDRATION

Equipment

100-mL beaker	magnetic stir bar
distillation apparatus	2 Pasteur pipets, with latex bulb
condenser, with tubing	5-mL sample vial
distilling head	sand bath[†]
10-mL round-bottom flask	13 × 100-mm test tube[‡]
receiver flask*	support ring
thermometer, –10 to 260 °C,	2 support stands
or equivalent, with adapter	3 utility clamps
vacuum adapter	wire gauze
10-mL graduated cylinder	

*10-mL vial or 10-mL round-bottom flask
[†]stirring hot plate with crystallizing dish filled with sand or magnetic stirrer and electric flask heater filled with sand
[‡]or centrifuge tube

Reagents and Properties

substance	quantity	molar mass (g/mol)	bp (°C)	d (g/mL)
calcium chloride anhydrous	0.25 g	110.99		
cyclohexanol	2.84 g	100.16	160	0.948
cyclohexene*		82.15	83	0.811
phosphoric acid, 85%	4.0 mL	98.00		1.685
sulfuric acid, concentrated	0.2 mL	98.08		1.840

* product

Preview

- Assemble the distillation apparatus
- Add cyclohexanol, sulfuric acid, and phosphoric acid to the flask
- Distill the reaction mixture and collect the distillate in a receiver
- Transfer the distillate to a test tube
- Remove the bottom layer of the distillate
- Dry the top layer with anhydrous calcium chloride

- Tare a sample vial
- Transfer the cyclohexene to the sample vial
- Weigh the cyclohexene

PROCEDURE

CHEMICAL ALERT

anhydrous calcium chloride—*irritant and hygroscopic*
cyclohexanol—*irritant and hygroscopic*
cyclohexene—*flammable and irritant*
phosphoric acid—*corrosive*
sulfuric acid—*toxic and oxidizer*

CAUTION

Wear departmentally approved safety goggles at all times while in the chemistry laboratory.

1. Using Distillation to Dehydrate Cyclohexanol

CAUTION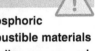

Concentrated sulfuric acid (H_2SO_4) is toxic and an oxidizer. Phosphoric acid (H_3PO_4) is corrosive. Prevent eye, skin, clothing, and combustible materials contact. Cyclohexanol is an irritant and hygroscopic. Avoid inhaling vapors and ingesting these compounds. Use a *fume hood*.

Assemble the distillation apparatus shown in Figure 5 on the next page. If necessary, use substitute glassware as directed by your laboratory instructor. Remove the 10-mL round-bottom flask from the apparatus. Place 4.0 mL of 85% H_3PO_4 and 2.84 g (3.0 mL) of cyclohexanol in the round-bottom flask. Add 5 drops of concentrated H_2SO_4 to the flask and add a magnetic stir bar.

Reattach the round-bottom flask to the distillation apparatus. Start the flow of water through the condenser.

Turn on the magnetic stirrer. Heat the reaction mixture while stirring until the product starts to distill. Continue the distillation, collecting the product in the receiver flask until no more liquid distills or until the temperature of the thermometer rises above 85 °C.

Turn off the heat. Allow the apparatus to cool. Turn off the magnetic stirrer.

Remove the receiver flask from the distillation assembly. Use a Pasteur pipet to transfer the distillate into a centrifuge tube or small test tube.

2. Isolating Cyclohexene

CAUTION

Cyclohexene is flammable and irritating. Keep away from flames or other heat sources. Prevent eye, skin, and clothing contact. Avoid inhaling vapors. Use a *fume hood*.

Notice that as the distillate in the tube cools, two layers form. Use the Pasteur pipet to remove the majority of the bottom layer. Place the

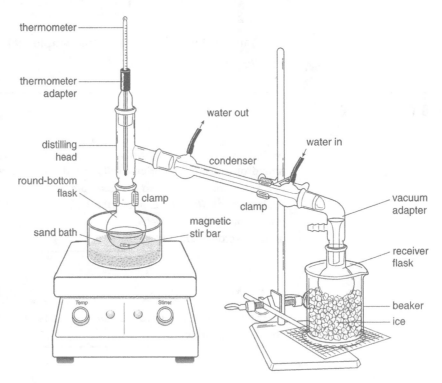

Figure 5
Distillation apparatus for semi-microscale dehydration

bottom layer into the container labeled "Recovered Acid Layer", provided by your laboratory instructor.

CAUTION

Anhydrous calcium chloride is irritating and hygroscopic. Avoid inhaling dust.

Dry the top organic layer by placing about 0.25 g of anhydrous calcium chloride into the test tube. Let the test tube stand for 5 min.

Weigh a clean 5-mL sample vial. Using a clean dry Pasteur pipet, remove the liquid from the test tube, and transfer the liquid to the tared sample vial. Weigh your product.

Characterize your cyclohexene using the methods in the Product Characterization section designated by your laboratory instructor.

3. Cleaning Up

Place your recovered materials in the appropriate labeled collection containers as directed by your laboratory instructor. Clean your glassware with soap or detergent.

CAUTION

Wash your hands thoroughly with soap or detergent before leaving the laboratory.

MICROSCALE DEHYDRATION

**Using Glassware with
Elastomeric Connectors**

Equipment

100-mL beaker	2 Pasteur pipets, with latex bulb
distillation apparatus	receiver vial
elastomeric connectors	5-mL sample vial
distilling head–air condenser	sand bath*
5-mL round-bottom flask	support ring
thermometer, −10 to 260 °C,	support stand
or equivalent	10 × 75-mm test tube[†]
10-mL graduated cylinder	2 utility clamps
magnetic stir bar	wire gauze

*stirring hot plate with crystallizing dish filled with sand or magnetic stirrer and electric flask heater filled with sand
[†]or centrifuge tube

Reagents and Properties

substance	quantity	molar mass (g/mol)	bp (°C)	d (g/mL)
calcium chloride, anhydrous	0.25 g	110.99		
cyclohexanol	1.422 g	100.16	160	0.948
cyclohexene*		82.15	83	0.811
phosphoric acid, 85%	1.5 mL	98.00		1.685
sulfuric acid, concentrated	0.12 mL	98.08		1.840

* product

Preview

- Assemble the distillation apparatus
- Add cyclohexanol, sulfuric acid, and phosphoric acid to the flask
- Distill the reaction mixture and collect the distillate in a receiver
- Transfer the distillate to a test tube
- Remove the bottom layer of the distillate
- Dry the top layer with anhydrous calcium chloride
- Tare a sample vial
- Transfer the cyclohexene to the sample vial
- Weigh the cyclohexene

PROCEDURE

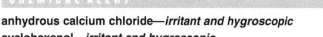

CHEMICAL ALERT

anhydrous calcium chloride—*irritant and hygroscopic*
cyclohexanol—*irritant and hygroscopic*
cyclohexene—*flammable and irritant*

phosphoric acid—*corrosive*

sulfuric acid—*toxic and oxidizer*

CAUTION

Wear departmentally approved safety goggles at all times while in the chemistry laboratory.

---

1. Using Distillation to Dehydrate Cyclohexanol

CAUTION

Concentrated sulfuric acid (H_2SO_4) is toxic and an oxidizer. Phosphoric acid (H_3PO_4) is corrosive. Prevent eye, skin, clothing, and combustible materials contact. Cyclohexanol is an irritant and hygroscopic. Avoid inhaling vapors and ingesting these compounds. Use a *fume hood*.

Assemble the distillation apparatus shown in Figure 6. Remove the 5-mL round-bottom flask from the apparatus. Place 1.5 mL of 85% H_3PO_4 and 1.422 g (1.5 mL) of cyclohexanol into the flask. Add 3 drops of concentrated H_2SO_4 to the flask and add a magnetic stir bar. Reattach the round-bottom flask to the distillation apparatus.

Turn on the magnetic stirrer. Heat the reaction mixture while stirring until the product starts to distill. Continue the distillation, collecting the product in the receiver vial until no more liquid distills or until the temperature of the thermometer rises above 85 °C.

Turn off the heat. Allow the apparatus to cool. Turn off the magnetic stirrer.

Remove the receiver vial from the distillation assembly. Use a Pasteur pipet to transfer the distillate into a centrifuge tube or small test tube.

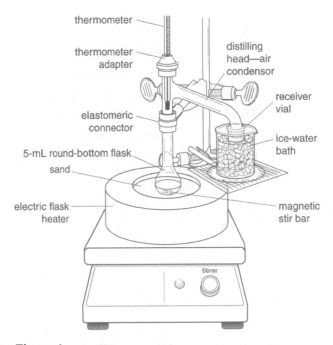

Figure 6
Distillation apparatus for microscale dehydration using glassware with elastomeric connectors

2. Isolating Cyclohexene

CAUTION

Cyclohexene is flammable and irritating. Keep away from flames or other heat sources. Prevent eye, skin, and clothing contact. Avoid inhaling vapors. Use a *fume hood*.

Notice that as the distillate in the tube cools, two layers form. Use the Pasteur pipet to remove the majority of the bottom layer. Place the bottom layer into the container labeled "Recovered Acid Layer", provided by your laboratory instructor.

CAUTION

Anhydrous calcium chloride is irritating and hygroscopic. Avoid inhaling dust.

Dry the top organic layer by placing about 0.25 g of anhydrous calcium chloride in the test tube. Let the test tube stand for 5 min.

Weigh a clean 5-mL sample vial. Using a clean dry Pasteur pipet, remove the liquid from the tube and transfer the liquid to the tared sample vial. Weigh your product.

Characterize your cyclohexene using the methods in the Product Characterization section designated by your laboratory instructor.

3. Cleaning Up

Place your recovered materials in the appropriate labeled collection containers as directed by your laboratory instructor. Clean your glassware with soap or detergent.

CAUTION

Wash your hands thoroughly with soap or detergent before leaving the laboratory.

MICROSCALE DEHYDRATION

Using a Hickman Still Assembly

Equipment

5-mL conical vial
10-mL graduated cylinder
Hickman still
magnetic spin vane
2 Pasteur pipets, with latex bulb
3-mL sample vial
sand bath*

support stand
10 × 75-mm test tube[†]
thermometer, −10 to 150 °C,
  with adapter[‡]
thermometer, −10 to 260 °C,
  or equivalent
2 utility clamps

*stirring hot plate with crystallizing dish filled with sand or magnetic stirrer and electric flask heater filled with sand
[†]or centrifuge tube
[‡]to fit Hickman still

Reagents and Properties

substance	quantity	molar mass (g/mol)	bp (°C)	d (g/mL)
calcium chloride anhydrous	0.25 g	110.99		
cyclohexanol	1.422 g	100.16	160	0.948
cyclohexene*		82.15	83	0.811
phosphoric acid, 85%	1.5 mL	98.00		1.685
sulfuric acid, concentrated	0.12 mL	98.08		1.840

* product

Preview

- Assemble the distillation apparatus
- Add cyclohexanol, sulfuric acid, and phosphoric acid to the vial
- Distill the reaction mixture into the still collar
- Transfer the distillate to a test tube
- Remove the bottom layer of the distillate
- Dry the top layer with anhydrous calcium chloride
- Tare a sample vial
- Transfer the cyclohexene to the sample vial
- Weigh the cyclohexene

PROCEDURE

CHEMICAL ALERT

anhydrous calcium chloride—*irritant and hygroscopic*
cyclohexanol—*irritant and hygroscopic*
cyclohexene—*flammable and irritant*
phosphoric acid—*corrosive*
sulfuric acid—*toxic and oxidizer*

CAUTION

Wear departmentally approved safety goggles at all times while in the chemistry laboratory.

1. Using Distillation to Dehydrate Cyclohexanol

CAUTION

Concentrated sulfuric acid (H_2SO_4) is toxic and an oxidizer. Phosphoric acid (H_3PO_4) is corrosive. Prevent eye, skin, clothing, and combustible materials contact. Cyclohexanol is an irritant and hygroscopic. Avoid inhaling vapors and ingesting these compounds. Use a *fume hood*.

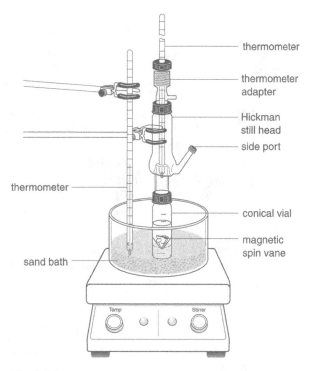

Figure 7
Distillation apparatus for microscale dehydration using a Hickman still

Assemble the distillation apparatus shown in Figure 7.

Remove the 5-mL conical vial from the apparatus. Place 1.5 mL of 85% H_3PO_4 and 1.422 g (1.5 mL) of cyclohexanol into the vial. Add 3 drops of concentrated H_2SO_4 to the vial and add a magnetic spin vane. Reattach the vial to the distillation apparatus.

Turn on the magnetic stirrer. Heat the reaction mixture while stirring until the product starts to distill. As the product starts to collect in the still, use a Pasteur pipet to remove the liquid from the still. [NOTE 1] Transfer the liquid into a centrifuge tube or a small test tube. Continue the distillation and collection until no more liquid distills or until the temperature of the thermometer rises above 85 °C.

Turn off the heat. Allow the apparatus to cool. Turn off the magnetic stirrer.

NOTE 1: If your Hickman still is not equipped with a side port, prepare a bent-tip Pasteur pipet as directed by your laboratory instructor.

2. Isolating Cyclohexene

CAUTION

Cyclohexene is flammable and irritating. Keep away from flames or other heat sources. Prevent eye, skin, and clothing contact. Avoid inhaling vapors. Use a *fume hood*.

Notice that as the distillate in the test tube or vial cools, two layers form. Use the Pasteur pipet to remove the majority of the bottom layer. Place the bottom layer into the container labeled "Recovered Acid Layer", provided by your laboratory instructor.

CAUTION

Anhydrous calcium chloride is irritating and hygroscopic. Avoid inhaling dust.

Dry the top organic layer by placing about 0.25 g of anhydrous calcium chloride into the test tube. Let the test tube stand for 5 min.

Weigh a clean 3-mL sample vial. Using a clean dry Pasteur pipet, remove the liquid from the test tube and transfer the liquid to the tared sample vial. Weigh your product.

Characterize your cyclohexene using the methods in the Product Characterization section designated by your laboratory instructor.

3. Cleaning Up

Place your recovered materials in the appropriate labeled collection containers as directed by your laboratory instructor. Clean your glassware with soap or detergent.

CAUTION

Wash your hands thoroughly with soap or detergent before leaving the laboratory.

PRODUCT CHARACTERIZATION

Equipment

5 Pasteur pipets, with latex bulb   white spot plate
3 test tubes, 10 × 75-mm

Reagents and Properties

substance	quantity	molar mass (g/mol)	bp (°C)
ammonium cerium(IV) nitrate test reagent	0.6 mL		
bromine test reagent	0.24 mL		
cyclohexanol	0.16 mL	100.16	160
cyclohexene	0.16 mL	82.15	83
dichloromethane	2.4 mL	84.93	40
1,4-dioxane	0.36 mL	88.11	100–102

Preview

- Test standards and product for presence of alcohol using ammonium cerium(IV) nitrate reagent

- Test standards and product for presence of alkene using bromine reagent

- Compare cyclohexanol and cyclohexene product using infrared analysis

- Measure refractive index of cyclohexene product

PROCEDURE

ammonium cerium(IV) nitrate—*irritant and oxidizer*
bromine—*highly toxic and oxidizer*
cyclohexanol—*irritant and hygroscopic*
cyclohexene—*flammable and irritant*
dichloromethane—*toxic and irritant*
1,4-dioxane—*flammable and suspected carcinogen*

Wear departmentally approved safety goggles at all times while in the chemistry laboratory.

1. Using Ammonium Cerium(IV) Nitrate to Test for Alcohols

Ammonium cerium(IV) nitrate, $(NH_4)_2Ce(NO_3)_6$, is irritating and an oxidizer. 1,4-Dioxane is flammable and a suspected carcinogen. Keep 1,4-dioxane away from flames or other heat sources. Prevent eye, skin, and clothing contact. Avoid inhaling vapors. Use 1,4-dioxane in a *fume hood*.

Cyclohexanol is irritating and hygroscopic. Cyclohexene is flammable and irritating. Keep cyclohexene away from flames or other heat sources. Prevent eye, skin, and clothing contact. Avoid inhaling vapors.

NOTE 2: 1,4-Dioxane is used as a solvent.

Place 5 drops of the $(NH_4)_2Ce(NO_3)_6$ test reagent and 3 drops of 1,4-dioxane in each of three wells of a white spot plate. [NOTE 2] Add 2 drops of cyclohexanol to the first well and stir. Observe any color change and record your results.

Add 2 drops of cyclohexene from the reagent bottle to the second well and stir. Observe any color change and record your results.

Add 2 drops of your cyclohexene product to the third well and stir. Observe any color change and record your results.

2. Using Bromine to Test for Alkenes

Bromine (Br_2) is highly toxic. Dichloromethane is toxic and irritating. Cyclohexanol is irritating and hygroscopic. Cyclohexene is flammable and irritating. Keep cyclohexene away from flames or other heat sources. Prevent eye, skin, and clothing contact. Avoid inhaling vapors. Use these reagents in a *fume hood*.

NOTE 3: Dichloromethane is used as a solvent.

Label three small test tubes "cyclohexanol", "cyclohexene", and "product". Place 2 drops of cyclohexanol into the tube labeled "cyclohexanol". Place 2 drops of cyclohexene into the tube labeled "cyclohexene". Place 2 drops of your product into the tube labeled "product".

Add 20 drops of dichloromethane into each test tube, and stir. [NOTE 3]. Add 2 drops of the Br_2 test reagent to each tube and stir. Observe any color change. Record your results.

Table 1 *Refractive indices (20 °C)*

water	1.3329
cyclohexanol	1.4650
cyclohexene	1.4460

3. Using Infrared Analysis to Compare Cyclohexanol and Your Cyclohexene Product

NOTE 4: Salt plates are fragile and hygroscopic. *Do not use water to wipe the plates.* Even moisture from your fingers will attack the plates. Use gloves and only handle the plates by the edges.

Obtain the operating instructions for using the infrared spectrometer from your laboratory instructor. Obtain a set of KBr, NaCl, or AgCl salt plates and a holder. [NOTE 4] Place 1 drop of your cyclohexanol between the salt plates. Gently press the plates together to remove any air bubbles. Place the plates in the holder and secure the plates. Run and plot the IR spectrum according to your operating instructions.

Repeat this procedure for your cyclohexene product. Examine the region of the spectrum above 1500 cm^{-1}. Assign the bonds that give rise to these absorptions.

4. Using Refractive Index to Characterize Your Cyclohexene Product

Obtain the operating instructions for the refractometer from your laboratory instructor. Measure the refractive index for your cyclohexene product. Measure the laboratory temperature in °C. Make temperature corrections, if necessary. [NOTE 5] Compare your refractive index to the literature values shown in Table 1.

5. Cleaning Up

NOTE 5: The refractive index at 20 °C is calculated by using the following equation, where T is the ambient temperature in degrees Celsius and n_D^T is the refractive index measured at ambient temperature.

$$n_D^{20} = n_D^T + 0.00045(T - 20\,°C)$$

Place your recovered materials in the appropriate labeled collection containers as directed by your laboratory instructor. Clean your glassware with soap or detergent.

CAUTION

Wash your hands thoroughly with soap or detergent before leaving the laboratory.

Name   Section   Date

Post-Laboratory Questions

1. Calculate the percent yield that you obtained from this reaction.

2. Did your product cause a color change with $(NH_4)_2Ce(NO_3)_6$ test reagent? Explain your results.

3. Did your product cause a color change with the Br_2 test reagent? Explain your results.

4. Compare the IR spectra for cyclohexanol and your product. What IR evidence do you have that your product is cyclohexene and not cyclohexanol? Briefly explain.

5. (a) Calculate the refractive index of your product at 20 °C.

   (b) Compare the refractive index of your product to the data of Table 1. Does the result indicate that your product is pure? Briefly explain.

   (c) If the refractive index of your product differs from the listed value, what is the most likely contaminant in your product, as indicated by the refractive index? Briefly explain.

6. What would be the major product obtained from the E1 dehydration of 2-methylcyclohexanol?

7. Outline a mechanism for the dehydration of 1-methyl-1-cyclohexanol. Would you predict this reaction to be faster or slower than the reaction you performed?

_____   _____   _____

Name   *Section*   *Date*

Pre-Laboratory Assignment

1. What safety precautions must be observed when using concentrated H_2SO_4 and H_3PO_4?

2. (a) Write the chemical equation for the dehydration of cyclohexanol.

(b) Using the following information, calculate the theoretical yield for the dehydration of 3.0 mL of cyclohexanol.

substance	molar mass (g/mol)	d (g/mL)
cyclohexanol	100.16	0.948
cyclohexene	82.15	0.811

3. When 2-butanol undergoes E1 dehydration, three alkenes are obtained. Draw the structures for these alkenes. Which alkene would you predict to be formed in greatest abundance?

ANAL `0727`

Classifying an Unknown Compound by Functional Group

Prepared by Jan William Simek, California Polytechnic State University

PURPOSE OF THE EXPERIMENT

Identify the functional group in an unknown organic compound by solubility tests and qualitative chemical tests.

BACKGROUND REQUIRED

You should be familiar with techniques for weighing, measuring by volume, and mixing in a test tube.

BACKGROUND INFORMATION

Organic qualitative analysis is an exercise in spectroscopy. Nuclear magnetic resonance spectroscopy and infrared spectroscopy are the major spectroscopic techniques used by organic chemists. However, much insight can be gained from using simple qualitative tests to determine the identity of unknowns. Structures of unknown compounds can be determined by comparing physical properties, performing functional group tests, and checking melting points of derivatives against those of known compounds reported in the literature. Solubility properties and chemical reactivity become apparent during these qualitative tests.

Organic qualitative analysis involves four types of tests.

1. *Measurement of physical properties* includes determining refractive index, boiling points, melting points, and density.

2. *Solubility tests* can suggest the size and polarity of an unknown compound and the presence of basic or acidic functional groups. A compound's solubility in aqueous acid or base involves ionization of the compound and, therefore, a chemical reaction. The salts produced are water-soluble.

3. *Chemical tests* transform an unknown into a different compound with an accompanying change in appearance. These tests are often called

classification tests because they identify the possible functional groups present.

4. *Formation of a solid derivative* is a critical step in identifying an unknown. Many compounds have similar physical properties and give similar results in qualitative tests. However, an unknown can undergo reaction to form another compound called a **derivative**. The melting point of the purified derivative allows identification of the unknown.

Unknown, monofunctional organic compounds can be classified into their functional group categories. For this experiment, the possible categories are alkane, alkene, alkyl halide, alcohol, phenol, amine, aldehyde, ketone, and carboxylic acid. Each of these functional groups has a unique combination of solubility and reactivity that allows it to be distinguished from the others. The results of solubility tests reduce the number of classification tests that must be conducted.

Solubility Tests

Organic compounds follow three interdependent rules of solubility:

1. *small organic molecules are more soluble in water than are large organic molecules;*

2. *polar organic molecules, especially those capable of hydrogen bonding, are more soluble in water than are nonpolar molecules; and*

3. *compounds in their ionic forms are more soluble in water than their neutral forms.*

For example, benzoic acid is not soluble in water, yet it is soluble in sodium hydroxide solution and in sodium hydrogen carbonate solution because these bases react with benzoic acid to form the water-soluble benzoate ion. The solubility of carboxylic acids and amines is so characteristic that solubility tests alone differentiate these functional groups from all the others in this experiment.

The solubility flowchart shown in Figure 1 provides the scheme for this experiment. The first test to perform on all unknowns is water solubility.

Water

Small, polar organic compounds such as alcohols, aldehydes, ketones, amines, carboxylic acids, and a few phenols are soluble in water. Water-soluble compounds are tested with pH paper to see if they are acidic or basic. A pH of 4 or lower indicates a carboxylic acid. A pH of 8 or higher indicates an amine.

Water-soluble compounds are tested with 5% sodium hydrogen carbonate ($NaHCO_3$) to determine whether or not they are carboxylic acids. Carboxylic acids react with $NaHCO_3$ to produce carbon dioxide bubbles, as shown below in Equation 3.

Large alcohols, aldehydes, ketones, amines, carboxylic acids, and phenols are not soluble in water. Alkanes, alkyl halides, and alkenes are not soluble in water, regardless of their size. These water-insoluble compounds are tested for their solubility in the following reagents.

5% Sodium Hydroxide

Water-insoluble compounds are first tested with 5% sodium hydroxide (NaOH). Sodium hydroxide is a strong base that ionizes strong or weak

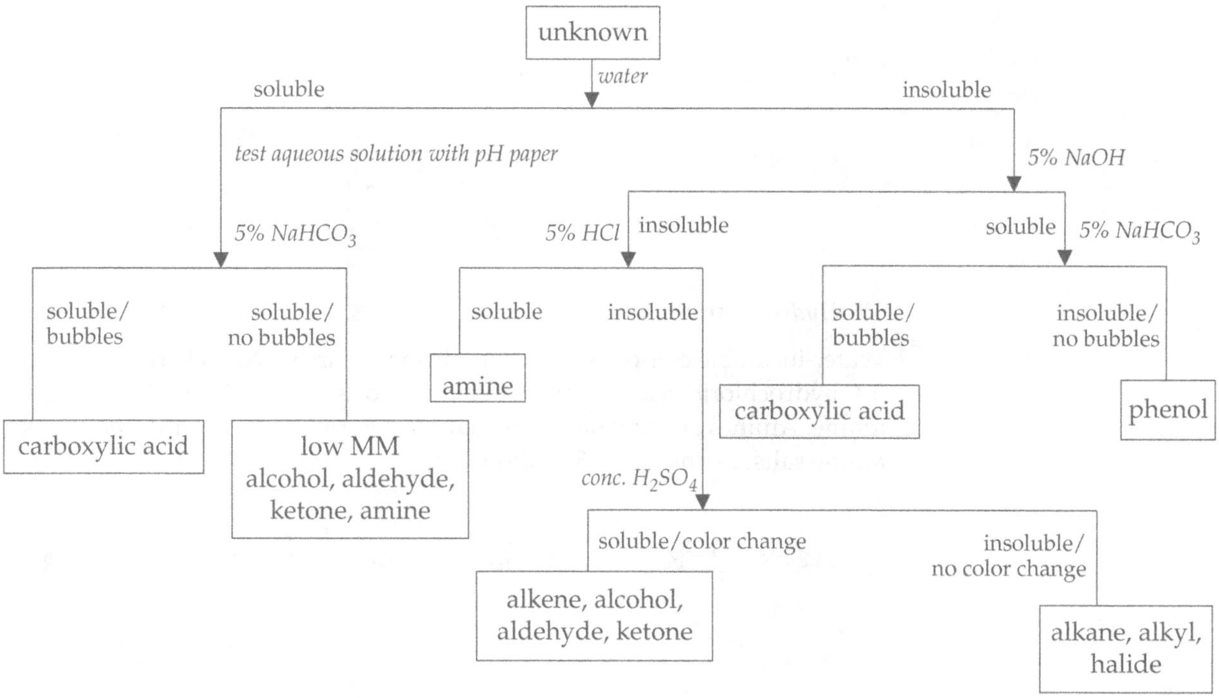

Figure 1
Solubility flowchart

acids. Thus, both carboxylic acids and phenols are converted to salts and dissolve in aqueous solution. Non-acidic compounds will not dissolve. The reactions of carboxylic acids and phenols are shown in Equations 1 and 2, respectively.

$$R{-}\overset{\overset{\displaystyle O}{\|}}{C}{-}OH \ + \ NaOH(aq) \ \longrightarrow \ R{-}\overset{\overset{\displaystyle O}{\|}}{C}{-}O^-Na^+ + \ H_2O \qquad (Eq.\ 1)$$

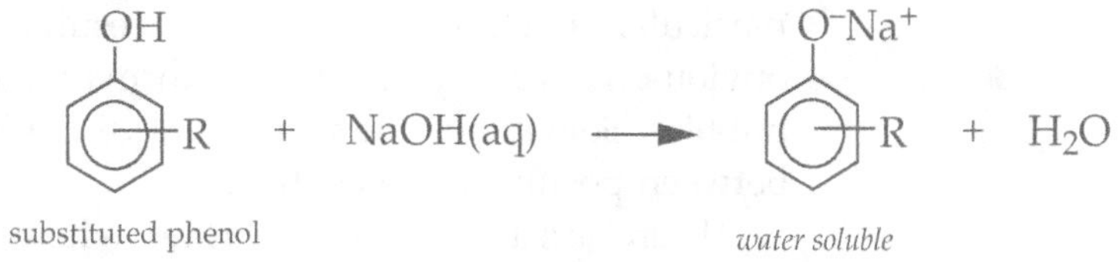

carboxylic acid $\qquad\qquad\qquad\qquad$ *water soluble*

$$\text{substituted phenol} + NaOH(aq) \longrightarrow \text{(water soluble)} + H_2O \qquad (Eq.\ 2)$$

5% Sodium Hydrogen Carbonate

Water-insoluble compounds that are soluble in 5% NaOH are then tested with 5% sodium hydrogen carbonate (NaHCO$_3$). Strongly acidic compounds such as carboxylic acids react with NaHCO$_3$ to form water-soluble salts, as shown in Equation 3. The reaction also produces bubbles of carbon dioxide (CO$_2$).

This test is commonly misinterpreted because the CO$_2$ bubbles are tiny. Careful observation is essential.

Phenols are less acidic than carboxylic acids and do not react with NaHCO$_3$ to form water-soluble salts. As a result, phenols are insoluble in 5% NaHCO$_3$.

$$R-\overset{\overset{\displaystyle O}{||}}{C}-OH \ + \ NaHCO_3(aq) \ \longrightarrow \ R-\overset{\overset{\displaystyle O}{||}}{C}-O^-Na^+ \ + \ H_2CO_3$$

carboxylic acid   *water soluble*

$$\longrightarrow \ R-\overset{\overset{\displaystyle O}{||}}{C}-O^-Na^+ \ + \ H_2O \ + \ CO_2 \qquad (Eq.\ 3)$$

water soluble   *bubbles*

5% Hydrochloric Acid

Water-insoluble compounds that are insoluble in 5% NaOH are tested with 5% hydrochloric acid (HCl). If a compound is soluble in 5% HCl, it is an amine. Amines are organic bases that react with HCl to form water-soluble amine salts, as shown in Equation 4.

$$R-\overset{\overset{\displaystyle ..}{N}}{\underset{\displaystyle R}{|}}-R \ + \ HCl(aq) \ \longrightarrow \ R-\overset{\overset{\displaystyle H}{|}}{\underset{\displaystyle R}{N^+}}-R \ \ Cl^- \qquad (Eq.\ 4)$$

amine   *water soluble*

Concentrated Sulfuric Acid

Water-insoluble compounds that are insoluble in 5% HCl are tested with concentrated sulfuric acid (H_2SO_4). Virtually all organic compounds containing alkene functional groups or oxygen or nitrogen atoms are soluble in concentrated H_2SO_4. These functional groups typically react with H_2SO_4 to form new compounds. Only alkanes, alkyl halides, and some aromatic compounds are insoluble in H_2SO_4.

Classification Tests

Solubility tests alone can indicate whether an unknown compound in this experiment is a carboxylic acid, a phenol, or an amine. The other functional groups must be identified or verified by classification tests.

Classification tests are based on the chemical reactivity characteristic of particular functional groups. The results are intended to be visual and obvious, such as a color change, formation of a precipitate, or evolution of bubbles. Sometimes the results are difficult to interpret or are borderline between positive and negative.

There are two inviolable rules when performing classification tests. First, perform the test exactly as described. If the procedure says add 3 drops, do not add 4 or 5. Second, always perform tests in triplicate. Perform the test on a known compound that will result in a positive test (**known positive**); perform the test on a known compound that will result in a negative test (**known negative**); and perform the test on the unknown compound. This direct visual comparison of the results of testing the unknown against a known positive test and a known negative test confirms that the reagents are good and you are performing the test properly.

No classification test is always accurate in every case. A compound may produce a **false positive** if the test is positive even though the compound giving the test *is not* of the expected type. For example, some phenols give a positive test for aldehydes. A **false negative** occurs if the test is negative even though the compound undergoing the test *is* the expected type.

For example, less reactive aldehydes or very insoluble aldehydes may fail to give a positive test for aldehydes.

The following classification tests are performed in this experiment and are among those tests commonly performed in qualitative organic analysis.

Bromine in Cyclohexane

Alkenes react with bromine (Br_2) in cyclohexane, an orange solution, to produce colorless vicinal dibromides, as shown in Equation 5. This test is commonly used for water-insoluble compounds. Alkenes with strong electron-withdrawing groups may fail to react. Phenols, phenyl ethers, and some aldehydes and ketones also react to decolorize bromine in cyclohexane.

$$\underset{alkene}{\diagdown C = C \diagup} \quad + \quad \underset{orange}{Br_2} \quad \xrightarrow{\text{cyclohexane solvent}} \quad \underset{colorless}{-\overset{\displaystyle |}{\underset{\displaystyle Br}{C}} - \overset{\displaystyle Br}{\underset{\displaystyle |}{C}} -} \qquad \text{(Eq. 5)}$$

Potassium Permanganate

Alkenes are oxidized to diols by dilute potassium permanganate ($KMnO_4$), as shown in Equation 6. The purple color of $KMnO_4$ disappears and is replaced by the brown color of manganese dioxide (MnO_2). Because $KMnO_4$ is a strong oxidizing agent, aldehydes, some primary and secondary alcohols, phenols, and aromatic amines can also react.

$$\underset{alkene}{\diagdown C = C \diagup} \quad + \quad \underset{purple}{KMnO_4(aq)} \quad \longrightarrow \quad \overset{OH\ \ OH}{\underset{}{-\overset{\displaystyle |}{C} - \overset{\displaystyle |}{C} -}} \quad + \quad \underset{brown}{MnO_2} \qquad \text{(Eq. 6)}$$

Silver Nitrate in Ethanol

Alkyl halides react with silver nitrate ($AgNO_3$) in ethanol by the S_N1 mechanism. Tertiary, allylic, and benzylic halides give an immediate precipitate at room temperature, as shown in Equation 7. Secondary halides require several minutes to give a precipitate, and primary halides require hours.

$$\underset{\text{alkyl halide}}{R-X} + AgNO_3 + HOCH_2CH_3 \longrightarrow R-OCH_2CH_3 + HNO_3 + \underset{precipitate}{AgX(s)} \qquad \text{(Eq. 7)}$$

Sodium Iodide in Acetone

A saturated solution of sodium iodide (NaI) in acetone reacts rapidly with primary, allylic, and benzylic chlorides or bromides by the S_N2 mechanism. Secondary halides react slowly, while tertiary halides are unreactive. The corresponding alkyl iodides and a precipitate of sodium chloride or sodium bromide result, as shown in Equation 8.

$$\underset{X = Br, Cl}{R-X} + NaI \xrightarrow{\text{acetone}} R-I + \underset{precipitate}{NaX(s)} \qquad \text{(Eq. 8)}$$

Beilstein Test

An organic halide placed on a copper wire and then exposed to a flame produces the blue–green flame of the volatile copper halide.

TCICA Test

In acid solution, 1,3,5-trichloroisocyanuric acid (TCICA) slowly releases chlorine, which is an oxidizing agent. The reaction is rapid in the presence of an oxidizable compound such as a primary or secondary alcohol, as shown in Equation 9. The product is isocyanuric acid, which is very soluble in water but precipitates from the solvent acetonitrile. The time it takes for isocyanuric acid precipitate to appear is characteristic of the type of alcohol. Secondary alcohols react fastest, within 15–30 seconds; primary alcohols produce a precipitate usually within 3–7 minutes, although some can take up to 20 minutes; tertiary alcohols are not oxidizable at room temperature and produce no precipitate within an hour.

alcohol   TCICA   carbonyl compound   isocyanuric acid *precipitate*

Iron(III) Chloride

Many phenols react with iron(III) chloride ($FeCl_3$) solution to give brightly colored complexes. Many of these complexes are short-lived; the color may fade soon after it forms. Some phenols may not react at all, so a negative iron(III) chloride test is inconclusive. Aldehydes or ketones with significant enolic character can also give colored complexes with $FeCl_3$.

Bromine in Water

Phenols are activated toward electrophilic aromatic substitution and react with Br_2 in the absence of catalyst, as shown in Equation 10. The disappearance of the bromine color, and often the appearance of a precipitate of the brominated phenol, constitute a positive test. Other activated aromatic compounds, such as phenyl ethers and anilines, can also react with Br_2.

phenol   *orange*   *usually* $n = 1–3$ *colorless*

2,4-Dinitrophenylhydrazine

Aldehydes and ketones rapidly form yellow, orange, or red precipitates with 2,4-dinitrophenylhydrazine (DNP) reagent, as shown in Equation 11.

$$\underset{\substack{\text{aldehyde or}\\\text{ketone}}}{\overset{O}{\underset{}{R-\overset{||}{C}-R'}}} + \underset{\text{2,4-dinitrophenylhydrazine}}{H_2N-NH-C_6H_3(NO_2)_2} \xrightarrow{H^+} \underset{\substack{\text{a 2,4-dinitrophenylhydrazone}\\\text{(a 2,4-DNP derivative)}\\\textit{red to yellow solid}}}{R-\overset{||}{\underset{R'}{C}}=N-NH-C_6H_3(NO_2)_2} + H_2O \quad (\text{Eq. 11})$$

Tollens Silver Mirror Test

Aldehydes are easily oxidized by silver ion, a mild and selective oxidizing agent. This reaction works best in basic solution. However, silver salts precipitate in basic solution unless ammonia is present to form the diaminesilver(I) complex ion, as shown in Equation 12. As shown in Equation 13, silver ion is reduced to silver metal, which plates out on *clean* glass, producing a mirror.

Some aldehydes are slow to react and require a few minutes to produce a silver mirror. Occasionally, the silver appears as a heavy black precipitate instead of adhering to the glass as a mirror.

$$Ag^+ + 2NH_3\,(aq) \longrightarrow Ag(NH_3)_2{}^+\,(aq) \quad (\text{Eq. 12})$$

$$\underset{\text{aldehyde}}{\overset{O}{\overset{||}{R-C-H}}} + 2\,Ag(NH_3)_2{}^+\,OH^- \xrightarrow[\text{H}_2\text{O}]{\text{NH}_3}$$

$$\overset{O}{\overset{||}{R-C-O^-NH_4{}^+}} + 2Ag\,(s) + 3NH_3\,(aq) + H_2O \quad (\text{Eq. 13})$$

In this experiment, you will identify two unknowns by functional groups using solubility tests and classification tests. Tables 1 and 2 list known positive and known negative compounds for solubility tests and classification tests.

Equipment

250-mL beaker	microspatula
Bunsen burner	glass stirring rod
copper wire	6–10 test tubes, 15 × 125-mm
10-mL graduated cylinder	6–10 test tubes, 10 × 75-mm
hot plate	test tube rack
pH paper	thermometer, −10 to 260 °C
1.0-mL transfer pipet	tongs
Pasteur pipet, with latex bulb	

Table 1 *Known positive and known negative test compounds for solubility tests*

	liquid compound		solid compound	
solvent	positive test	negative test	positive test	negative test
water	glycerol	benzaldehyde	2,2-dimethyl-1,3-propanediol	benzoic acid
5% NaOH	eugenol	benzaldehyde	vanillin	biphenyl
5% NaHCO$_3$	octanoic acid	benzaldehyde	benzoic acid	biphenyl
5% HCl	diisobutylamine	benzaldehyde	4-N,N-dimethyl-aminobenzaldehyde	biphenyl
H$_2$SO$_4$	cyclohexene	cyclohexane	vanillin	biphenyl

Table 2 *Known positive and known negative test compounds for functional group classification tests*

functional group	test	liquid compound		solid compound	
		positive test	negative test	positive test	negative test
alkane	by exclusion—alkanes are insoluble in aqueous reagents and in H_2SO_4, and are negative for alkyl halide tests				
alkene	bromine/cyclohexane	cyclohexene	cyclohexane	none	none
	$KMnO_4$	cyclohexene	cyclohexane	none	none
alkyl halide	Beilstein	1-bromohexane	2-propanol	none	none
	$AgNO_3$/ethanol	2-chloro-2-methylpropane	2-propanol	none	none
	NaI/acetone	1-bromohexane	2-propanol	none	none
alcohol	TCICA test	2-propanol	2-chloro-2-methylpropane	2,2-dimethyl-1,3-propanediol	benzoic acid
phenol (to confirm)	$FeCl_3$	eugenol	benzyl alcohol	vanillin	benzoic acid
	bromine/H_2O	2-isopropylphenol	2-propanol	2-naphthol	benzoic acid
amine	soluble in HCl—this group is determined by the series of solubility tests: if water insoluble, then soluble in HCl				
aldehyde	2,4-DNP	benzaldehyde	1-butanol	piperonal	benzoic acid
	Tollens test	benzaldehyde	1-butanol	piperonal	4-methoxy-acetophenone
ketone	2,4-DNP	acetone	1-butanol	4-methoxy-acetophenone	benzoic acid
carboxylic acid	soluble in NaOH and in $NaHCO_3$—this group is determined by the series of solubility tests: if water-soluble, solution is acidic to pH paper; if water-insoluble, then soluble in NaOH and soluble in $NaHCO_3$ with gas evolution				

Reagents and Properties (amounts estimated for two unknowns)

substance	quantity	molar mass (g/mol)	mp (°C)	bp (°C)
acetone	10 mL	58.1		56
acetonitrile	1 mL	41.0		82
ammonium hydroxide, conc.	6 mL	17.0		
benzaldehyde	1 mL	106.1		179
benzoic acid	1 g	122.1	123	
benzyl alcohol	0.2 mL	108.1		205
biphenyl	0.5 g	154.2	72	255
bromine in water, satd.	6 mL	159.8		
1-bromohexane	0.2 mL	165.1		158
1-butanol	0.5 mL	74.1		118
2-chloro-2-methylpropane	0.2 mL	92.6		52
cyclohexane	8 mL	84.2		81
cyclohexene	0.25 mL	82.2		83
diethyl ether	6 mL	74.1		35
diisobutylamine	0.2 mL	129.2		139
4-(dimethyl-amino) benzaldehyde	0.1 g	149.2	75	
2,2-dimethyl-1,3-propanediol	0.2 g	104.2	127	
2,4-dinitrophenylhydrazine	2 mL			
ethanol, 95%	6 mL	46.1		78
eugenol	0.2 mL	164.2		254
iron(III) chloride, 3%	1 mL	162.2		
glycerol	0.2 mL	92.1	20	182
hydrochloric acid, 5%	6 mL	36.5		
2-isopropylphenol	0.2 mL	136.2	16	213
4-methoxyacetophenone	0.2 g	150.2	38	
2-methyl-2-propanol	0.5 mL	74.1	26	83
2-naphthol	0.1 g	144.2	123	286
nitric acid, 3M	10 mL	63.0		
octanoic acid	0.2 mL	144.2	16	237
piperonal	0.2 g	150.1	37	264
potassium permanganate, 1%	0.5 mL	158.0		
2-propanol	0.5 mL	60.1		82
silver nitrate, 5%	12 mL	169.9		
silver nitrate in ethanol, 2%	6 mL	169.9		
sodium hydrogen carbonate, 5%	6 mL	84.0		
sodium hydroxide, 5%	6 mL	40.0		
sodium iodide in acetone	6 mL	149.9		
sulfuric acid, concentrated	6 mL	98.1		
TCICA in acetonitrile, 3%	3 mL	232.4	251	
unknown organic compound	1 mL/1 g			
vanillin	0.5 g	152.2	83	

Preview

- Perform the water solubility test on the known positive, known negative, and unknown
- Perform subsequent solubility tests
- If the solubility tests point to a carboxylic acid or amine, the classification is complete
- If the solubility tests suggest any other functional groups, perform the classification tests appropriate to those groups until the unknown is narrowed to only one functional group

PROCEDURE

CAUTION

Wear departmentally approved safety goggles at all times while in the chemistry laboratory.

    Always use caution in the laboratory. Many chemicals are potentially harmful. Follow safety precautions given for all reagents used in this experiment. Prevent contact with your eyes, skin, and clothing. Avoid ingesting any of the reagents.

Perform all tests in triplicate using an unknown, a known positive, and a known negative. Mix well to make certain that liquid samples are not floating at the meniscus. Allow several minutes for compounds to dissolve. Be patient and observe closely.

    Conduct the solubility tests following the pattern shown in Figure 1 earlier in this experiment. *Verify your solubility test results with your laboratory instructor before performing the classification tests.* Conduct the classification tests indicated by your solubility results. Use clean test tubes for each test.

1. Performing the Water Solubility Test

CAUTION

Unknowns may be flammable, toxic, corrosive, or irritating. Keep away from flames or other heat sources.

Add 2–3 drops of a liquid sample or about 50 mg of a solid sample to 1 mL of distilled or deionized water in a test tube. Tap the tube with your finger to mix or stir gently with a glass stirring rod. Record the sample as soluble or insoluble.

    If the unknown is water-soluble, test the solution with pH paper. Also test the pH of water as a control.

    A solution at pH 4 or lower suggests a carboxylic acid. A solution at pH 8 or higher suggests an amine.

2. Performing the 5% Sodium Hydroxide Solubility Test

CAUTION

Sodium hydroxide (NaOH) and hydrochloric acid (HCl) are toxic and corrosive.

If your compound is water-soluble, proceed to Part 3.

For water-insoluble compounds, add 2–3 drops of a liquid sample or about 50 mg of a solid sample to 1 mL of 5% NaOH in a test tube. Tap the tube with your finger to mix or stir gently with a glass stirring rod. Record the sample as soluble or insoluble.

To verify that a compound has dissolved, add 5% HC1 to the NaOH mixture until the solution is acidic to pH paper. Look for a precipitate, indicating that the water-soluble salt has converted back into the water-insoluble compound.

Solubility in NaOH indicates either a carboxylic acid or phenol.

3. Performing the 5% Sodium Hydrogen Carbonate Solubility Test

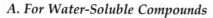

A. For Water-Soluble Compounds

Put 2–3 drops of liquid sample or about 50 mg of solid sample in a dry test tube. Add 1 mL of 5% sodium hydrogen carbonate ($NaHCO_3$). Do not stir. Watch for bubbles at the interface of the phases. Then tap the tube with your finger to mix or stir gently with a glass stirring rod. Record the sample as soluble or insoluble.

Generation of bubbles and solubility indicates a carboxylic acid. Solubility without generation of bubbles indicates a low molar mass alcohol, aldehyde, ketone, or amine. Conduct classification tests to determine which functional group is present.

CAUTION

Diethyl ether (ether) is highly flammable and toxic. Keep away from flames or other heat sources. Use a *fume hood*.

If no bubbles were observed, put 2–3 drops of liquid sample or about 50 mg of solid sample in a dry test tube. Using a *fume hood,* add about 1 mL of ether. Then immediately add 1 mL of 5% $NaHCO_3$. Observe whether or not bubbles are generated at the ether–water interface.

Generation of bubbles indicates a carboxylic acid.

B. For Water-Insoluble Compounds

Put 2–3 drops of liquid sample or about 50 mg of solid sample in a dry test tube. Add 1 mL of 5% sodium hydrogen carbonate ($NaHCO_3$). Do not stir. Watch for bubbles at the interface of the phases. Then tap the tube with your finger to mix or stir gently with a glass stirring rod. Record the sample as soluble or insoluble.

Generation of bubbles or solubility indicates a carboxylic acid.

If the compound is not soluble in $NaHCO_3$ but is soluble in NaOH, it is likely a phenol. Confirm the presence of phenol with a phenol classification test.

4. Performing the 5% Hydrochloric Acid Solubility Test

CAUTION

Hydrochloric acid (HCl) is toxic and corrosive.

For compounds insoluble in water and insoluble in 5% NaOH, add 2–3 drops of a liquid sample or about 50 mg of a solid sample to 1 mL of 5% HCl in a test tube. Tap the tube with your finger to mix or stir gently with a glass stirring rod. Record the sample as soluble or insoluble.

If the compound is soluble in 5% HCl, it is most likely an amine.

5. Performing the Concentrated Sulfuric Acid Solubility Test

CAUTION

Concentrated sulfuric acid (H_2SO_4) is toxic and oxidizing. Use a *fume hood* when working with H_2SO_4.

If the compound is insoluble in 5% HCl and 5% NaOH, add 2-3 drops of a liquid sample or about 50 mg of a solid sample to 1 mL of concentrated sulfuric acid (H_2SO_4) in a dry test tube. Tap the tube with your finger to mix or stir gently with a glass stirring rod. Do not use a metal spatula.

Record the sample as soluble or insoluble. Interpret a color change or a precipitate as soluble.

If the compound is soluble in H_2SO_4, the sample is an alkene, an alcohol, an aldehyde, or a ketone. Conduct classification tests for each compound type.

If the compound is insoluble in H_2SO_4, the sample is an alkane or an alkyl halide. Conduct classification tests for alkyl halides.

If alkyl halide tests are negative, the compound is an alkane.

6. Performing the Bromine in Cyclohexane Test for Alkenes

CAUTION

Bromine (Br_2) is toxic and oxidizing. It causes severe burns. Always use a *fume hood* when working with Br_2. Acetone and cyclohexane are flammable and irritating. Keep away from flames or other heat sources.

Place 1 mL of cyclohexane in a small test tube. Add 3 drops of Br_2/H_2O. Mix until the bromine color appears in the top cyclohexane layer.

For liquid samples, add 2 drops of sample to the Br_2/H_2O. Tap the tube with your finger to mix or stir gently with a glass stirring rod. Note and record whether or not the orange color disappears.

For solid samples, place 30 mg of solid into a test tube. Add 5 drops of acetone. Add the acetone solution to the Br_2/H_2O. Tap the tube with your finger to mix or stir gently with a glass stirring rod. Note and record whether or not the orange color disappears.

NOTE 1: Phenols, phenyl ethers, and some aldehydes and ketones may test positive.

If the orange color disappears quickly, the sample may be an alkene. [NOTE 1]

7. Performing the Potassium Permanganate Test for Alkenes

CAUTION

1% Potassium permanganate ($KMnO_4$) is corrosive and oxidizing.

If your sample is water-soluble, place 1–2 mL of water into a small test tube. If your sample is water-insoluble, place 1–2 mL of 95% ethanol into a small test tube.

Add 2 drops of a liquid sample or about 30 mg of a solid sample. Add 2 drops of 1% $KMnO_4$. Tap the tube with your finger to mix or stir gently

NOTE 2: The brown color or precipitate may not appear. Aldehydes, some primary and secondary alcohols, phenols, and aromatic amines may test positive.

with a glass stirring rod. Let the mixture stand 10–20 s. Note and record whether or not the purple color disappears.

If the purple color disappears and a brown color or precipitate appears, the compound may be an alkene. [NOTE 2]

8. Performing the Silver Nitrate in Ethanol Test for Alkyl Halides

CAUTION

Silver nitrate (AgNO₃) in ethanol is flammable, toxic, and oxidizing. It also stains the skin. Keep away from flames or other heat sources.

Place 1 mL of 2% $AgNO_3$ in ethanol into a small test tube.

For liquid samples, add 2 drops of sample to the 2% $AgNO_3$. Tap the tube with your finger to mix or stir gently with a glass stirring rod.

For solid samples, place 30 mg of solid into a test tube. Add 5 drops of ethanol. Add this ethanol solution to the 2% $AgNO_3$ in ethanol. Tap the tube with your finger to mix or stir gently with a glass stirring rod. Note and record whether or not a precipitate forms.

An immediate precipitate indicates a tertiary, allylic, or benzylic halide.

9. Performing the Sodium Iodide in Acetone Test for Alkyl Halides

CAUTION

Sodium iodide (NaI) in acetone is flammable and irritating. Keep away from flames or other heat sources.

Place *exactly* 1.0 mL of NaI in acetone into a small test tube. Add 3 drops of a liquid sample. Tap the tube with your finger to mix or stir gently with a glass stirring rod. Allow the tube to stand 3–6 min at room temperature. Note and record whether or not a precipitate forms.

A white precipitate indicates a primary, allylic, or benzylic halide.

10. Performing the Beilstein Flame Test for Alkyl Halides

CAUTION

Make certain no flammable compounds are near when using a flame.

Obtain a coiled piece of pure copper wire from your laboratory instructor. Light a Bunsen burner. Using tongs, hold the copper wire in the flame to burn the wire clean. Remove the wire from the flame and allow the wire to cool for 1–2 min.

Use a dropper to put 1 drop of liquid sample or a few mg of a solid sample on the coiled wire. Quickly insert the wire into the lower part of the flame. Note and record the color of the flame.

A blue–green color indicates the presence of chlorine, bromine, or iodine in the compound.

11. Performing the TCICA Test for Alcohols

CAUTION

1,3,5-trichloroisocyanuric acid (TCICA) is corrosive and oxidizing. Acetonitrile is toxic. 5% Hydrochloric acid (HCl) is toxic and corrosive.

© 1999 Cengage Learning

Place 0.5 mL of the TCICA test solution into a small test tube. Add 1 drop of 5% HCl. Tap the tube with your finger to mix or stir gently with a glass stirring rod.

For liquid samples, add 1 drop of the sample. Tap the tube with your finger to mix or stir gently with a glass stirring rod.

For solid samples, dissolve about 20 mg of solid in 1–2 drops of acetonitrile. Add this solution to the TCICA/HCl solution.

Note and record whether or not a precipitate forms.

The formation of a precipitate within 1 min indicates a secondary alcohol; the formation of a precipitate between 3–20 min indicates a primary alcohol.

12. Performing the Iron(III) Chloride Test for Phenols

CAUTION

Iron(III) chloride (FeCl₃) is toxic and corrosive. Ethanol is flammable and toxic. Keep away from flames or other heat sources.

NOTE 3: Some aldehydes or ketones also give colored complexes with FeCl₃.

Place 1 mL of 95% ethanol into a small test tube. Add 2 drops of a liquid sample or about 30 mg of a solid. Add 3–5 drops of 3% FeCl₃. Tap the tube with your finger to mix or stir gently with a glass stirring rod. Note and record any formation of a brightly colored solution.

The presence of bright color, even briefly, indicates a phenol. [NOTE 3]

13. Performing the Bromine in Water Test for Phenols

CAUTION

Bromine (Br₂) is toxic and oxidizing. It causes severe burns. Always use a *fume hood* when working with Br₂. Ethanol is flammable. Keep away from flames or other heat sources.

Place 1 mL of 95% ethanol into a small test tube. Add 5 drops of a liquid sample or about 30 mg of a solid.

Add a drop of water. Tap the tube with your finger to mix or stir gently with a glass stirring rod.

Add 1 drop of Br₂/H₂O. Tap the tube with your finger to mix or stir gently with a glass stirring rod.

Note and record whether or not the orange color disappears.

The disappearance of the orange color indicates a phenol.

14. Performing the 2,4-DNP Test for Aldehydes and Ketones

CAUTION

2,4-Dinitrophenylhydrazine (2,4-DNP) solution is corrosive and irritating. It stains skin and clothing.

For liquid samples, place 1 drop of sample into a clean, dry test tube. Add up to 20 drops of 2,4-DNP solution. Tap the tube with your finger to mix or stir gently with a glass stirring rod.

For solid samples, add about 30 mg of solid into a clean, dry test tube. Add 0.5 mL of ethanol. Tap the tube with your finger to mix or stir gently with a glass stirring rod. If the unknown does not dissolve, prepare a warm-water bath by placing 175–200 mL of tap water into a 250-mL beaker.

Use a hot plate to heat the water to 40 °C. Place the test tube into a warm-water bath and swirl the tube until the unknown is dissolved. Cool the solution to room temperature. Add up to 20 drops of 2,4-DNP solution. Tap the tube with your finger to mix or stir gently with a glass stirring rod.

Note and record whether or not a precipitate forms.

An immediate, brightly colored precipitate indicates an aldehyde or ketone.

15. Performing the Tollens Silver Mirror Test for Aldehydes

CAUTION

Silver nitrate ($AgNO_3$) and nitric acid (HNO_3) are toxic and oxidizing. $AgNO_3$ will stain skin and clothing. Sodium hydroxide (NaOH) is toxic and corrosive. Ammonium hydroxide (NH_4OH) is corrosive and a lachrymator. Use a *fume hood* when working with NH_4OH.

NOTE 4: The test tubes must be *very clean* for a silver mirror to form.

Thoroughly wash 3 test tubes with soap and water. [NOTE 4] Rinse the test tubes with distilled or deionized water. Do not rinse the test tubes with acetone.

CAUTION

Prepare the Tollens reagent just before use. A highly explosive precipitate forms upon standing several hours. When you are finished with the Tollens tests, rinse each test tube with ~1 mL of 3*M* HNO_3 to destroy any residual Tollens reagent.

Add 2 mL of 5% $AgNO_3$ to each test tube. Add 1 mL of 5% NaOH solution to each test tube. In a *fume hood,* add concentrated NH_4OH dropwise, with mixing, until the black Ag_2O precipitate just dissolves.

For liquid samples, add 1 drop of liquid to the Tollens reagent. Tap the tube with your finger to mix or stir gently with a glass stirring rod. Allow the solution to stand for 5 min.

For solid samples, dissolve about 30 mg of solid in 0.5 mL ethanol. If necessary, heat the solution in a 40 °C warm-water bath to dissolve the sample. Cool the solution to room temperature. Add the sample solution to the Tollens reagent. Tap the tube with your finger to mix or stir gently with a glass stirring rod. Allow the solution to stand for 5 min.

Record whether or not a silver mirror or a black precipitate forms.

Formation of a silver mirror or heavy black precipitate indicates an aldehyde.

If there is no visible change within 5 min, place the tube in a 80 °C hot-water bath for 15 s. Allow the solution to stand for 5 min.

When the tests are complete, pour the contents of each tube into the "Recovered Silver Solution" container, provided by your laboratory instructor. Rinse each test tube with ~1 mL of 3*M* HNO_3 to destroy any residual Tollens reagent. Add this rinse to the "Recovered Silver Solution" container. Wash the test tubes with soap and water.

16. Cleaning Up

Use the labeled collection containers provided by your laboratory instructor.

Turn in your remaining unknown to your laboratory instructor. Clean your glassware with soap or detergent.

CAUTION

Wash your hands with soap or detergent before leaving the laboratory.

POST-LABORATORY QUESTIONS

1. Record the solubility results for each unknown that you tested. Describe your observations and briefly explain your conclusions.

2. Record the results of the classification tests that you conducted for each unknown you tested. Describe your observations and briefly explain your conclusions.

3. For each of your unknowns, list the functional group to which it belongs next to its identification code.

4. You suspect that your unknown contains halogen, so you perform the silver nitrate in ethanol test and the sodium iodide in acetone test, both of which are negative. Do these results prove that your compound does not contain a halogen? Briefly explain.

_____   _____   _____
Name   Section   Date

Pre-Laboratory Assignment

1. Why is it important to rinse test tubes used in the Tollens test with $3M$ HNO_3?

2. What risks do you run by not performing the qualitative tests in triplicate?

3. (a) Why is it important to have clean test tubes before running a test?

(b) Before which tests should acetone *not* be used to clean the test tubes?

4. Why is water solubility the first test to run?

5. Why run solubility tests before running the functional group classification tests?

6. Determine the functional group present in these unknowns:

(a) Unknown A is soluble in water and gives bubbles with 5% $NaHCO_3$.

(b) Unknown B is insoluble in water, insoluble in 5% NaOH, but soluble in 5% HCl.

(c) Unknown C is insoluble in water, insoluble in 5% NaOH, insoluble in 5% HCl, soluble with a color change in conc. H_2SO_4, and decolorizes both $KMnO_4$ (aq) and bromine in cyclohexane.

(d) Unknown D is soluble in water, does not produce bubbles with 5% $NaHCO_3$, gives a precipitate with 2,4-DNP, and gives a silver mirror in the Tollens test.

7. In each of the following cases, describe the *next* test you would perform.

(a) Unknown X is insoluble in water, 5% NaOH, 5% HCl, and conc. H_2SO_4.

(b) Unknown Y is insoluble in water, soluble in 5% NaOH, and insoluble in 5% $NaHCO_3$.

(c) Unknown Z is insoluble in water, insoluble in 5% NaOH, insoluble in 5% HCl, and soluble in conc. H_2SO_4.

8. If your unknown is soluble in water and does not produce bubbles with 5% $NaHCO_3$, what steps would you follow to determine if your unknown is an amine?

CPSIA information can be obtained
at www.ICGtesting.com
Printed in the USA
BVHW020348060723
666831BV00010B/241

9 781337 449236